NEBOSH NATIONAL GENERAL CERTIFICATE

UNIT NGC1: MANAGEMENT OF HEALTH AND SAFETY

Element 1: Foundations in Health and Safety

Element 2: Plan

Element 3: Do

Element 4: Check

Element 5: Act

Contributors

Dr J Phelpstead, BSc, PhD, CMIOSH

For information on all RRC publications and training courses, visit: www.rrc.co.uk

RRC: NGC1.4

ISBN for this volume: 978-1-911002-39-0

ISBN for complete set of 2 volumes: 978-1-911002-41-3

Fourth edition Autumn 2016

ACKNOWLEDGMENTS

RRC International would like to thank the National Examination Board in Occupational Safety and Health (NEBOSH) for their co-operation in allowing us to reproduce extracts from their syllabus guides.

This publication contains public sector information published by the Health and Safety Executive and licensed under the Open Government Licence v.2 (www.nationalarchives.gov.uk/doc/open-government-licence/version/2).

Every effort has been made to trace copyright material and obtain permission to reproduce it. If there are any errors or omissions, RRC would welcome notification so that corrections may be incorporated in future reprints or editions of this material.

Introduction

Element 1: Foundations in Health and Safety

Element 1: Foundations in Health and Safety (Continued)

Element 2: Plan

Element 3: Do

Element 3: Do (Continued)

Element 4: Check

Element 5: Act

Course Structure

This textbook has been designed to provide the reader with the core knowledge needed to successfully complete the NEBOSH National General Certificate in Occupational Health and Safety, as well as providing a useful overview of health and safety management. It follows the structure and content of the NEBOSH syllabus.

The NEBOSH General Certificate consists of three units of study. When you successfully complete any of the units you will receive a Unit Certificate, but to achieve a complete NEBOSH General Certificate qualification you need to pass the three units within a five-year period. For more detailed information about how the syllabus is structured, visit the NEBOSH website (www.nebosh.org.uk).

Unit NGC1: Management of Health and Safety	
Element 1	Foundations in Health and Safety
Element 2	Plan
Element 3	Do
Element 4	Check
Element 5	Act

Unit GC2: Controlling Workplace Hazards	
Element 1	Workplace Hazards and Risk Control
Element 2	Transport Hazards and Risk Control
Element 3	Musculoskeletal Hazards and Risk Control
Element 4	Work Equipment Hazards and Risk Control
Element 5	Electrical Safety
Element 6	Fire Safety
Element 7	Chemical and Biological Health Hazards and Risk Control
Element 8	Physical and Psychological Health Hazards and Risk Control
	Revision and Examination Guide

Unit GC3: Health and Safety Practical Application
The Practical Assessment

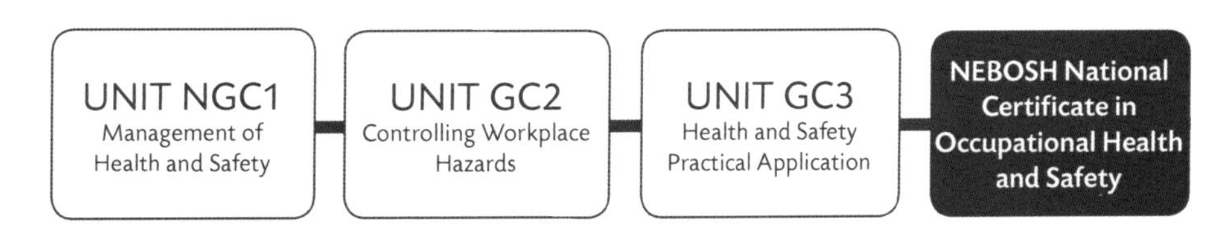

Assessment

To complete the qualification, you need to pass two formal written exams (one for Unit NGC1 and one for Unit GC2), as well as a safety inspection of your workplace, including a short report to management (Unit GC3).

Each written exam is two hours long and consists of one long question (20% of the marks) and ten short questions (each being 8% of the total marks). You must answer all questions.

More Information

As you work your way through this book, always remember to relate your own experiences in the workplace to the topics you study. An appreciation of the practical application and significance of health and safety will help you understand the topics.

Keeping Yourself Up to Date

The field of health and safety is constantly evolving and, as such, it will be necessary for you to keep up to date with changing legislation and best practice.

RRC International publishes updates to all its course materials via a quarterly e-newsletter (issued in February, May, August and November), which alerts students to key changes in legislation, best practice and other information pertinent to current courses.

Please visit www.rrc.co.uk/news/newsletters.aspx to access these updates.

Other Textbooks in the Series

- The Management of International Oil and Gas Health and Safety: A Guide to the NEBOSH International Technical Certificate in Oil and Gas Operational Safety (First Edition, June 2012)
- NEBOSH Award in Health and Safety at Work – ARABIC (First Edition, June 2012)

RRC International is continually adding to its range of textbooks. Visit www.rrc.co.uk/publishing for a full range of current titles.

Element 1

Foundations in Health and Safety

Learning Outcomes

Once you've read this element, you'll understand how to:

1. Outline the scope and nature of occupational health and safety.
2. Explain the moral and financial reasons for promoting good standards of health and safety in the workplace.
3. Explain the legal framework for the regulation of health and safety including sources and types of law.
4. Explain the scope, duties and offences of employers, managers, employees and others under the **Health and Safety at Work, etc. Act 1974.**
5. Explain the scope, duties and offences of employers, managers, employees and others under the **Management of Health and Safety at Work Regulations 1999**.
6. Outline the legal and organisational health and safety roles and responsibilities of clients and their contractors.
7. Outline the principles of assessing and managing contractors.

Contents

The Scope and Nature of Occupational Health and Safety

IN THIS SECTION...

- The study of health and safety involves the study of many different subjects, including the sciences (chemistry, physics and biology), engineering, psychology, sociology and law.
- There are many barriers to good standards of health and safety in a workplace: workplaces can be complex; there are often competing and conflicting demands placed upon people and organisations; and good health and safety practice often relies on the perfect behaviour of individuals, who sometimes fail to behave in this ideal way.
- Key definitions are:
  - **Health** - the absence of disease.
  - **Safety** - the absence of risk of serious personal injury.
  - **Welfare** - access to basic facilities that the worker needs for basic functions, e.g. toilets.

The Multi-Disciplinary Nature of Health and Safety

Workplace health and safety practice brings together knowledge from many different disciplines. Some health and safety topics are simple to understand; others are technical and require specialist knowledge. Sometimes the practical solution to a health and safety problem is straightforward; at other times the solution is complicated and demanding and requires the correct application of technical knowledge and thinking.

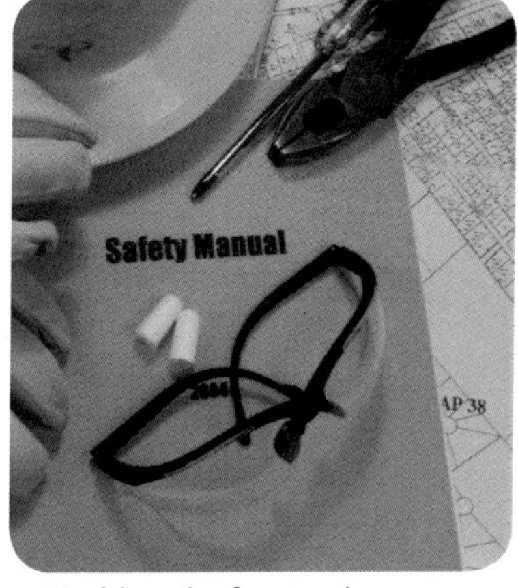

Health and safety involves many different disciplines

In order to fully understand a health and safety issue you need to be familiar with the:

- Technical background to the issue and have the relevant knowledge.
- Standards that may apply to the workplace and to the specific health and safety issue under consideration.
- Possible strengths and weaknesses of the various options that are available to solve the problem.

The study of health and safety therefore involves many different subjects, including the sciences (chemistry, physics and biology), engineering, psychology, sociology and law.

The Barriers to Good Standards of Health and Safety

There are many barriers to good standards of health and safety in a workplace:

- **Complexity** - workplaces can be complicated, involving the co-ordination of many people performing many different activities. Finding a solution to a specific health and safety problem or issue can be complex, requiring extensive background knowledge and an awareness of the possible consequences of the various courses of action that are available.
- **Conflicting demands** - there are often competing and conflicting demands placed upon people and organisations. A common conflict of interest is that between the need to supply a product or a service at an appropriate speed so as to make a profit, and the need to do so safely and without risk to people's health.

- Another conflict can be created by the need to comply with different types of standards at the same time, e.g. health and safety law.
- **Behavioural issues** - good health and safety practice often relies on the perfect behaviour of individuals, and people sometimes do not behave in this ideal way. We often solve health and safety problems by requiring workers to follow rules of procedure, e.g. a construction worker wearing a hard hat. But people are not robots; they do not behave as they are supposed to all the time. Workers sometimes make mistakes (they do the wrong thing thinking that it is the right thing to do). Sometimes they deliberately break the rules, falsely believing the end justifies the means.

The fact that health and safety standards are affected by worker behaviour can be a significant barrier to maintaining good standards in a workplace.

Behavioural issues - a worker ignores safety rules

Definitions

The topic of health and safety makes use of key words and phrases. Some important definitions are:

Health

The absence of disease or ill health. For example, asbestos creates a health risk because if you inhale asbestos dust you may contract lung cancer at some stage later in life (perhaps 20 or 30 years after you inhaled the dust). Health relates not only to physical ill health but also to psychological ill health, (e.g. exposure to extreme stress can lead to a nervous breakdown).

Safety

The absence of risk of serious personal injury. For example, walking under a load suspended from a crane during a lifting operation is not safe because, if the load falls, serious personal injury or death could result. Staying out of the danger area results in safety.

Welfare

Access to basic facilities such as toilet facilities, hand-wash stations, changing rooms, rest rooms and places where food can be prepared and eaten in relatively hygienic conditions, drinking water and basic first aid provision.

Welfare facilities - hand-wash stations

STUDY QUESTIONS

1. Why may health and safety not be seen as a priority by the management of an organisation?
2. Define:

   (a) Health.

   (b) Safety.

   (c) Welfare.

(Suggested Answers are at the end.)

The Moral and Financial Reasons for Health and Safety

IN THIS SECTION...

- The three main reasons why an organisation has to manage health and safety are: moral, economic and legal. In this section, two of these reasons are explored.
- The moral reason relates to the moral duty that one person has to another. Many people are killed, injured or made sick by their work. This is morally unacceptable and society expects good standards of health and safety.
- The financial reason relates to the fact that accidents and ill health cost money. When an accident occurs there will be direct and indirect costs associated with that event. Some of these losses can be insured against; many of them will be uninsured.

Organisations and individuals have to manage health and safety standards within the workplace for various reasons. These reasons can usually be grouped under three main headings: moral, financial and legal. In this section the first two reasons will be explored.

The Size of the Problem

The following statistics are compiled by the Health and Safety Executive (HSE). These figures represent five-year averages over recent years. Up-to-date figures can be obtained from the HSE website (www.hse.gov.uk). (You do not need to remember the actual figures; we give them to highlight the scale of the problem.)

Example of a workplace injury

On average, in Great Britain, every year:

- 155 workers are killed at work.
- 22,480 workers suffer a major/specified injury.
- 59,436 workers suffer an over-seven-day injury.
- 1.2 million people suffer from an illness they believe was caused or made worse by their current or past work.
- 27.5 million working days are lost:
  - 22.8m due to work-related ill health.
  - 4.7m due to workplace injury.
- Over 2,349 people die from mesothelioma.

These figures relate to the number of accidents and cases of disease which are reported and recorded. Inevitably, there will be under-reporting and under-recording, so the real figures are almost certainly higher, (e.g. the Labour Force Survey (which questions employees) estimates over 300,000 reportable injuries occur each year.

These statistics indicate that a huge amount of pain and suffering is experienced by people who simply go to work to earn a living. The numbers indicate the scale of the problem. What the numbers don't do is tell the individual stories. When health and safety is not managed properly people get killed and injured in gruesome ways or suffer terrible diseases that have a massive impact not only on them, but also their dependants, families, friends and colleagues. This suffering is morally unacceptable.

Employers (through management) provide the premises and equipment and put in place the working practices which employees use to produce the goods and services with which employers earn profits. To that extent, employers can be said to gain from the conditions at the workplace. In return, they provide an income for employees, but also have a moral responsibility to provide safe and healthy working conditions.

Societal Expectation

Standards of health and safety improve over time. Court cases indicate how a simple requirement such as "safe place of work" has changed over the years. What was considered a safe workplace in 1960 is very different from that which is expected in the current decade. Societal expectations change as society changes, for example:

- Well-designed and reliable equipment, a comfortable workplace, organised systems of work and a high level of training are standards that people take for granted now because they are so common.
- Widespread access to knowledge now ensures that anyone interested in legal standards or best practice can find the relevant information.
- Media coverage now ensures that when poor standards of health and safety are revealed, this is broadcast to society quickly and by many different methods.

Though individuals may appear not to be interested in health and safety, when a serious injury or disease is caused by work the overall response from society is one of condemnation.

The Business Case for Health and Safety

The business case for health and safety is simply that accidents and ill health cost an employer money. When an accident occurs there will be direct and indirect costs associated with that event. Some of these losses can be insured against, but many cannot. The financial impact of accidents and ill health can have significant effects on the profitability of an organisation and, in some cases, can lead to bankruptcy.

When an accident occurs, there are two types of losses that the organisation may face:

- **Direct costs** - the measurable costs arising directly from the accident.
- **Indirect costs** - those which arise indirectly as a consequence of the event. Indirect costs are often difficult to quantify precisely and may be hard to identify. In certain circumstances they may be extremely high.

TOPIC FOCUS

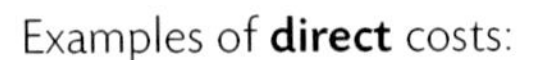

Examples of **direct** costs:

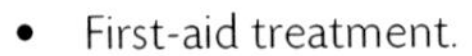

- First-aid treatment.
- Employee sick pay.
- Repairs to, or replacement of, damaged equipment and buildings.
- Lost or damaged product.
- Lost production time whilst dealing with the injury.
- Overtime to make up for lost time.
- Costs associated with the rehabilitation of the injured employee and their return to work.
- Fines in the criminal courts.
- Compensation payable to the victim, which is likely to be met by insurance cover and will therefore result in an increase in insurance premiums.

(Continued)

TOPIC FOCUS

Examples of **indirect** costs:

- Loss of staff from productive duties in order to investigate the incident, prepare reports, undertake hospital visits, deal with relatives, attend court proceedings.
- Loss of staff morale (which impacts on productivity and efficiency).
- Cost of remedial action following an investigation, e.g. change of process or materials and/or the introduction of further control measures.
- Compliance with any enforcement notice served.
- Cost of recruiting and training temporary or replacement labour.
- General difficulties in recruiting and retaining staff as an indirect result of the accident.
- Loss of goodwill of customers following delays in production and fulfilling orders.
- Activation of penalty clauses for failing to meet delivery dates.
- Damage to public image and business reputation.
- Damage to industrial relations, perhaps leading to industrial action, (e.g. strikes).

From the examples given you can see that, though more difficult to identify, the indirect costs associated with a workplace accident can be very large indeed.

Insured and Uninsured Costs

It is usually possible to take out insurance to cover some of the losses that might foreseeably occur to an organisation. It is compulsory to take out **employers' liability insurance** (under the **Employers' Liability (Compulsory Insurance) Act 1969**), so that if an employee is killed or injured at work there is insurance in place to pay them (or their dependants) compensation. The minimum amount of cover is currently £5 million. The current certificate must be 'displayed' for the benefit of employees (though this can be made available in electronic form) and produced if required by an inspector.

Similarly, it is usual for an employer to insure their premises and stock against fire. However, it is not possible to insure against all losses. Some losses are uninsurable by their very nature. For example, you cannot take out an insurance policy to pay money should you be prosecuted and fined in the criminal law courts, as it would no longer act as an effective deterrent. Other losses are not insured because the loss is too difficult to quantify or because the insurance would be too expensive to consider. For example, organisations cannot insure themselves against loss of revenue if their business reputation is damaged through a major workplace accident. There is no law that prevents this type of insurance, it is simply impossible to obtain.

Many of the direct and indirect costs associated with workplace accidents are uninsured for these reasons. It has been estimated that uninsured losses are between eight and 36 times greater than insured losses. Examples of possible uninsured losses include:

- Loss of raw materials due to accidents.
- Sick pay for injured workers.
- Overtime to make up for lost production.
- Repair to damaged equipment.

MORE...

www.hse.gov.uk/statistics/index.htm

www.hse.gov.uk/business/index.htm

It is worth remembering that most insurance policies come with an excess and with a limit. The excess is the amount of money that will be payable by the organisation before any payment is forthcoming from the insurer (for example, the first £5,000 of any claim). The limit is the cap above which the insurer will not pay (for example, if you have £2 million fire insurance but it costs £3 million to re-build your premises, then the insurer will only pay the first £2 million, the remaining sum is uninsured).

STUDY QUESTIONS

3. In three words, sum up the reasons why an organisation should manage health and safety.
4. Give examples of how societal expectations can result in higher standards of health and safety.
5. Give three direct costs and three indirect costs that might arise from a workplace accident.

(Suggested Answers are at the end.)

The Legal Framework for Regulating Health and Safety

IN THIS SECTION...

- Two types of law create a framework for the regulation of health and safety: criminal law and civil law.
- Criminal law is concerned with the punishment of companies or individuals who have broken statute health and safety law.
- Civil law is concerned with the compensation of people who have been injured or made ill in work-related incidents through no fault of their own.
- Two sources of law are used in the criminal and civil systems: statute law and common law.
- Statute law is made by Parliament in the form of Acts and Regulations.
- Common law is made by judges through the precedents that they set by their decision-making.
- The law courts used for criminal and civil cases are different and there is a clear hierarchy to the court system, with the Supreme Court sitting as the highest court in the land.
- The enforcement of statute health and safety law is carried out by several authorities such as the Health and Safety Executive (HSE).
- HSE inspectors have many powers under the **Health and Safety at Work, etc. Act 1974** (**HSWA**) to investigate and examine workplaces. They can also issue Enforcement Notices or prosecute in the criminal courts.
- The two types of Enforcement Notice are the Improvement Notice and the Prohibition Notice. Certain conditions have to be met before an inspector can issue either notice. The employer can appeal against these notices to an Employment Tribunal.
- Successful prosecution of a company or an individual under **HSWA** can lead to unlimited fines and/or imprisonment up to 6 months at Magistrates' Court, or unlimited fines and/or 2 years' imprisonment at Crown Court.
- The **Corporate Manslaughter and Corporate Homicide Act 2007** allows organisations that have caused death through gross negligence to be prosecuted and fined for their offence.
- The civil legal system is concerned with claims for compensation brought using the Tort of Negligence.
- For negligence to be proved, three tests have to be met: a duty of care had to be owed by the defendant to the claimant; that duty must have been breached; a loss must have occurred as a direct result.
- An important principle in the civil legal system is vicarious liability, which means that the employer can be held liable for the negligent acts of his employees.
- There are various defences against a claim of negligence, one of which is the principle of contributory negligence; that the claimant was partly to blame for their own injury and so should not be awarded full compensation.

Criminal and Civil Law

Two main types of law create a framework for the regulation of health and safety; criminal and civil law. Before examining each type in detail it is worth outlining some general principles and characteristics of this framework.

TOPIC FOCUS

The table summarises the two types of law and shows some of the significant differences between the two.

Criminal law	Civil law
Action is brought by the state.	Action is brought by the individual.
The intention is punishment.	The intention is compensation.
There is usually no time limit within which legal proceedings have to start.	Legal proceedings have to start within 3 years of the date of injury.
Insurance is not available to pay the fine.	Insurance is available to pay the compensation.
Statute law is used as the source of law.	Common law is used as the source of law.
The burden of proof is normally on the prosecution to prove "guilt beyond reasonable doubt".	The burden of proof is on the claimant to prove their case "on balance of probabilities".

A simple workplace accident can trigger both types of legal action. For example, imagine a scenario where an employee is run over by a forklift truck and suffers multiple broken bones.

The **criminal law** implications might be:

- This accident might be investigated by a Health and Safety Executive (HSE) inspector. The HSE are an enforcing authority acting on behalf of the state.
- They might decide to prosecute the company involved, for a breach of the **Health and Safety at Work, etc. Act 1974 (HSWA)** (i.e. for a breach of statute law).
- Any prosecution would be done on behalf of the state and the court papers would reflect this (the case would be recorded as Regina (the Crown) - versus - the organisation).
- If the organisation were found guilty of an offence they would be fined. The fine cannot be reclaimed from an insurance company and it is not an allowable business expense, (i.e. it cannot be written off against tax). This is the punishment for breaking the law.

The intention of the criminal legal system is to punish those who break the law. (It is important that justice is seen to be done; the punishment has a deterrent effect on the organisation involved and on other organisations who might also be breaking the law.) However, it does not necessarily help the injured employee. If the injured employee in this scenario wants financial compensation for an injury that was not their fault, then they will have to turn to the civil legal system.

The **civil law** implications might be:

- The injured employee sues their employer for compensation.
- To do this they instruct a solicitor to act on their behalf. The letter of claim to the employer has to be sent within **three years** of the date of the accident.
- If the case goes to court then the court papers will reflect that the employee is suing their employer; their name - versus - their employer's name will appear in the case records.
- In the court the employee's legal team can use **common law** to support their case.

- The employee will need to show that their employer was liable for their accident **on balance of probabilities**.
- If the employee wins then the court decides how much **compensation** should be paid. This compensation is paid from the employer's **insurance** policy.

There are, of course, many complications and technicalities that are not reflected in the scenario above. For example, most claims for compensation are settled out of court between the injured party (the claimant) and the insurance company of the organisation, so no court case actually happens. Many occupational diseases take more than three years for symptoms to appear and therefore the three year rule cannot be applied from the date of exposure to the harm; it has to be applied to the date when the person first becomes aware that they have the disease, (i.e. three years from diagnosis to start the claim process). Sometimes, individuals rather than organisations are prosecuted in the criminal courts for offences under HSWA, and where this occurs, there is the possibility of a fine and/or imprisonment being handed down as punishment.

However, the above scenario and general characteristics are useful as a general frame on which more detailed information will be hung later in this element.

Sources of Law

There are two sources of law that are relevant to the criminal and civil legal systems outlined above; **statute law** and **common law**. Put simply, statute law is made by Parliament and exists in the form of Acts, Regulations and Orders. Common law is made by judges through the decisions that they make and the precedents that they set. It is, in effect, the law of the land as established by custom and practice.

Statute Law

- Acts

  The most important piece of statute law relating to health and safety in the workplace is, of course, **HSWA**. This is the primary piece of statute law for the course. Other Acts also impact on health and safety (such as the **Corporate Manslaughter and Corporate Homicide Act 2007**).

Two types of law create a framework for the regulation of health and safety

- Regulations

  HSWA is an enabling Act, meaning that it allows for the creation of health and safety regulations such as the **Management of Health and Safety at Work Regulations 1999 (MHSWR)**. These regulations are referred to as delegated (or secondary) legislation. There are dozens of sets of regulations made under **HSWA**.

- Approved Codes of Practice

  Approved Codes of Practice (ACoPs) often accompany regulations, (e.g. there is an ACoP for the **Control of Substances Hazardous to Health Regulations 2002**). ACoPs explain how to achieve the legal standard outlined in the regulations that they accompany and give a clear indication of what is expected. ACoPs do not have the full legal status of Acts or Regulations. Instead they have **special** or **semi-legal status**. Failure to comply with an ACoP can be used as evidence of failure to achieve legal standards. If an ACoP has not been complied with then it must be shown that alternative methods were used that achieve at least the same standard as the ACoP.

- Guidance

  Official guidance also often accompanies regulations, (e.g. there is guidance on the **Manual Handling Operations Regulations 1992**). Guidance has no legal status but is useful in interpreting legal standards. Guidance often sets out best practice.

- Relevance of Statute Law

  The **HSWA** and Regulations made under the Act are frequently used in bringing prosecutions in the criminal courts.

  However, the HSWA and regulations made under the Act are never used in bringing a claim for compensation in the civil court (the reason why, and the exception to this rule, will be outlined later).

Common Law

Common law is not recorded in the form of Acts and Regulations. Instead it is made up of decided cases. A court case requires a judge (or several judges) to make a decision and perhaps state the reasons for their decision. These reasons may then establish a precedent that will influence the decision-making of judges in the future. Common law is therefore recorded in the form of past court cases and the reasoning stated in those cases. Common law relies heavily on the principle of judicial precedent; the idea that judges in courts have to take note of and follow the precedents set in courts higher in the court hierarchy. Therefore, the Supreme Court (was House of Lords) sets binding precedents for all other courts.

- The Employer's Common Law Duties

  The common law duties of an employer were identified in general terms in the decided case of ***Wilsons and Clyde Coal Co. Ltd v. English (1938)***. The judgment established the common law duty of all employers to provide:

  - A safe place of work with safe access to and from it.
  - Safe plant and equipment.
  - A safe system for doing the work.
  - Safe and competent workers.
  - Appropriate supervision, information, instruction and training.

  These common law duties were later used as a basis for some of the statutory duties in **HSWA**.

- Relevance of Common Law

  Common law is routinely used in the civil courts when bringing a claim for compensation. However, it is not used when bringing prosecutions against employers for health and safety failings. In very rare cases, a prosecution may be brought against an individual on the basis of manslaughter by gross negligence. This is a common law offence.

Court Structure

England, Wales and Northern Ireland

The structure of the law courts reflects the fact that there are two separate types of law (criminal and civil). The general structure of the courts is outlined in the following diagram:

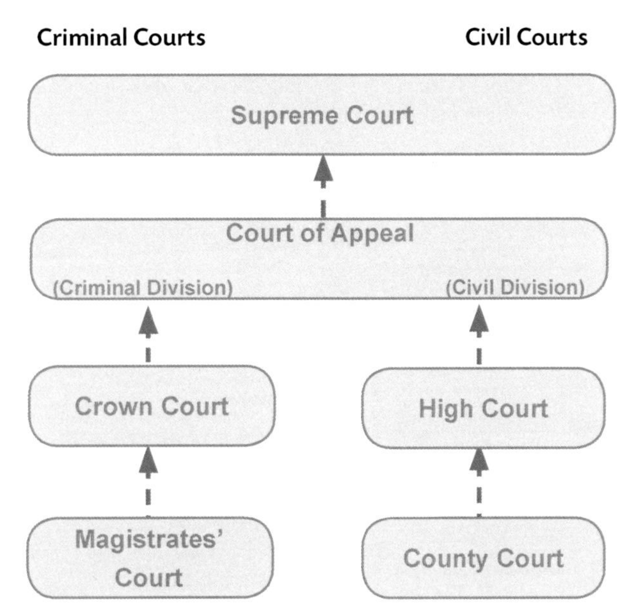

Criminal and Civil Courts in England, Wales and Northern Ireland

All criminal cases go to the Magistrates' Court in the first instance. More serious cases will then be sent up (indicted) to Crown Court. An appeal might then be made to the Court of Appeal (Criminal Division) (or the High Court for important points of law). Final appeal might then be allowed to the Supreme Court.

Civil cases will either go to the County Court or High Court depending on the amount of compensation being claimed. Typically, claims of less than £50,000 are settled in the County Court and more than £50,000 in the High Court. Any first appeal will go to the Court of Appeal (Civil Division). Final appeal might then be allowed to the Supreme Court.

Again, there are various technicalities and details, some of which will be discussed later in this element, but this general outline is useful as a starting point.

Apart from the obvious separation of the criminal and civil systems, two points should be noted:

- There is a clear hierarchy, with lower courts and higher courts. The higher a court is in the structure, the more influence the court has over courts lower down. For example, judges in the Court of Appeal get to set precedents that other judges in lower courts have to follow.
- The Supreme Court is the court of final appeal in almost all instances and can set precedents for all other courts. It straddles both systems.

HINTS AND TIPS

The court structure in Scotland is different from that found in other parts of the UK. Knowledge of both systems is not required, but knowledge of one system is. You are free to choose whichever system seems most appropriate to your needs.

Scotland

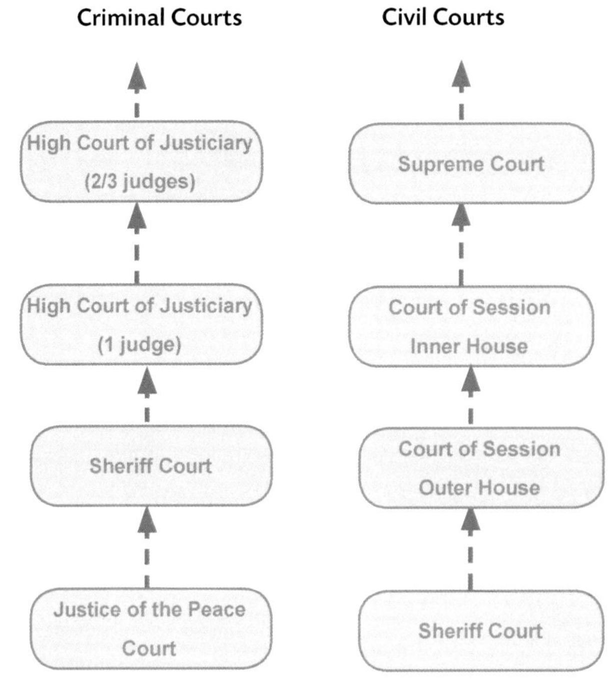

Criminal and Civil Courts in Scotland

The diagram above shows a simplified structure for the Scottish courts. Criminal cases go to the Justice of the Peace, Sheriff or High Court, depending on the severity of the offence. Appeals are then made to the next court up in the structure (except in the High Court where appeals are heard internally). Similarly, civil claims go to the Sheriff Court or Court of Session (depending on value) and appeals are heard by the next court up in the structure. Again, there is clear separation between civil and criminal courts and a clear hierarchy.

The Influence of the European Union

The European Union was created by the Treaty of Rome in 1957. One of the intentions of its creation was the easy exchange of goods and services between member states. To that end, there has been a significant drive to harmonise health and safety standards across Europe.

This harmonisation is achieved by the introduction of:

- **European Directives** – statutory instruments that require member states to achieve a certain legal standard through their own internal legislation within a timescale.
- **European Regulations** – statutory instruments that impose legal standards onto member states and take precedence over internal law.

A lot of health and safety legislation introduced in the UK (since 1992) has been driven by European Directives. For example, the **MHSWR** were first introduced to comply with such a directive.

UK law is influenced by European Directives

Criminal Law

The Enforcing Authorities

There are several authorities who have a role in enforcing health and safety law in the UK. First amongst these is the Health and Safety Executive (HSE) and its equivalent body in Northern Ireland, the Health and Safety Executive for Northern Ireland (HSENI).

The HSE enforces health and safety law in a wide range of workplaces. These include factories, mines, quarries, construction sites, off-shore oil and gas facilities, chemical plants and agriculture. These might be described as the medium- and high-risk workplaces. The HSE does not, however, enforce in all workplaces and it does not generally enforce fire safety legislation.

The HSE has a number of roles:

- Enforcement of **HSWA** and associated law.
- Reviewing existing legislation and making recommendations for changes.
- Providing information and guidance.
- Conducting research.

The HSE website is an excellent source of information on legal standards and best practice (www.hse.gov.uk).

Local authorities enforce health and safety law in many workplaces not covered by the HSE, such as hotels, restaurants, offices and depots. These might be described as lower-risk workplaces. Enforcement is carried out by Environmental Health Officers (EHOs) who have the same powers under **HSWA** as HSE inspectors.

Fire and Rescue authorities are the main enforcing agents for general fire precautions under the **Regulatory Reform (Fire Safety) Order 2005**. They have a number of enforcement options available to them, including issuing an alterations notice, enforcement notice, prohibition notice and prosecution. Fire Safety Inspectors have powers similar to those of HSE inspectors.

As well as these general authorities there are many others that may be involved depending on the nature of the workplace, its location and the nature of the law in question:

- The Office of Rail and Road (ORR) is the principal enforcer on the rail network.
- The Crown Prosecution Service (CPS) is involved in the decision-making process for manslaughter and corporate manslaughter prosecution in England and Wales.
- In Scotland the Procurators Fiscal carry out a similar role to the CPS.
- Some health and safety legislation is enforced by the environmental protection agencies; The Environment Agency in England, the Northern Ireland Environment Agency, Natural Resources Wales and the Scottish Environment Protection Agency.

In some countries, insurance companies fulfil a major role in enforcing safety. In the UK, their legal role is limited to inspecting certain items of equipment. However, the inspections and audits they undertake of their clients' premises supplement those of the authorities, and in some cases are the only inspections which occur on a regular basis. They can exert considerable influence in raising standards, as they can refuse to provide insurance cover unless their standards are met.

Powers of Inspectors under HSWA

Inspectors appointed under **HSWA** have wide-ranging powers to enter and inspect premises to ensure that activities are being carried out in accordance with the law.

Whilst the general policy is to promote compliance through co-operation and discussion, inspectors do have the power to issue enforcement notices and, if necessary, prosecute offenders.

TOPIC FOCUS

Under Section 20 of **HSWA** inspectors have the following powers:

- To enter premises, at any reasonable time.
- To take along a police officer if they believe they are going to be obstructed.
- To take along technical assistance or equipment if necessary.
- To carry out any necessary examinations and investigations.
- To direct that premises (in whole or in part) or items within the premises are left undisturbed.
- To take photographs, drawings and measurements.
- To take samples of articles or substances and of the atmosphere.
- To dismantle and/or test any item or substance which they think is dangerous.
- To take possession of articles and substances for examination or test, or as evidence in proceedings.
- To take statements from any person who might be able to help in their investigation. Interviewees must answer any questions and sign a statement of their answers (although these are not admissible as evidence in any subsequent proceedings against that person).
- To inspect and copy any document or record considered relevant.
- To receive access to reasonable facilities and assistance in conducting their investigation.
- Any other power necessary to fulfil the duty of their enforcement authority.

Section 25 of **HSWA** adds an additional power:

- To seize and render harmless (by destruction if necessary) any article or substance that gives rise to imminent danger of serious personal injury.

Enforcement Notices

There are two types of Enforcement Notice – **Improvement Notices** (issued under Section 21 of **HSWA**) and **Prohibition Notices** (issued under Section 22).

TOPIC FOCUS

Improvement Notices

- An Improvement Notice is issued where the inspector thinks that health and safety law is being breached or a breach has occurred and is likely to be repeated.
- It will only be issued if the inspector does not think there is a risk of serious personal injury.
- The Improvement Notice will state that an improvement must be made to achieve minimum legal standards and will impose a timescale that the inspector thinks is appropriate.
- The timescale for an Improvement Notice cannot be less than 21 days.
- The inspector may state the specific action needed to achieve legal compliance and make reference to any relevant ACoP or guidance.
- The Improvement Notice is served on the person in charge of the workplace or activity that is in breach; this is normally the employer.
- Any appeal against the notice must be made within 21 days.

So, for example, an inspector investigating a call centre where 30 staff work with Display Screen Equipment (DSE) for 9-hour shifts would expect to see DSE workstation assessments being conducted as required by the **Health and Safety (Display Screen Equipment) Regulations 1992**. They would also expect to see free eye tests being offered to employees. If these assessments and eye tests were not being provided then the inspector would be entitled to issue an Improvement Notice, requiring the employer to carry out the assessments and offer the free eye tests within a specified timescale, (e.g. 2 months), because:

- The relevant regulations are being breached.
- It is not a trivial matter in a call centre.
- No-one is at risk of imminent serious personal injury.

TOPIC FOCUS

Prohibition Notices

- A Prohibition Notice is issued where the inspector thinks that there is a risk of serious personal injury.
- The Prohibition Notice will state that the activity must be stopped until such time as it has been remedied.
- No timescale is specified.
- The inspector does not need to see a breach of health and safety law.
- The Prohibition Notice is served on the person in control of the activity; this is often the employer.
- Any appeal against the Notice must be made within 21 days.

So, for example, an inspector investigating an engineering factory where a large guard covering a dangerous moving part of machinery is missing might issue a Prohibition Notice. Any person coming into contact with that moving part might be pulled into the machinery and suffer a very serious injury or even be killed. The machine must immediately be taken out of use and cannot be re-used until it has been made safe, (e.g. by fitting the relevant guards).

Appeals Against Enforcement Notices

Appeals against Notices are made to an **employment tribunal**. The appeal must be in writing and state the grounds for the appeal.

The main grounds for an appeal are:

- There has been a wrong legal interpretation by the inspector.
- The inspector has exceeded his powers.
- A breach of the law is admitted, but the suggested remedy or timescale is not practicable or reasonably practicable (we will discuss this further in the following section of this element).
- A breach of law is admitted, but it is insignificant.

For an Improvement Notice, bringing an appeal **suspends** the notice until the appeal is heard or withdrawn.

For a Prohibition Notice, the prohibition **remains in place** unless the tribunal directs otherwise.

The decision of the tribunal may be to:

- Cancel the notice.
- Affirm (uphold) the notice.
- Affirm and modify the notice, (e.g. by extending the timescale).

The emphasis is upon simplicity and speed. Often, in order to speed up the procedure, a tribunal will order a preliminary hearing to see if the matter can be resolved between the parties without a full tribunal taking place.

Failure to Comply

Failure to comply with an Enforcement Notice can result in a fine and/or a prison sentence. Maximum penalties are:

- **Magistrates' Court:**
  - unlimited fine and/or
  - 6 months' prison.
- **Crown Court:**
  - unlimited fine and/or
  - 2 years' prison.

Fines can be unlimited

Fee for Intervention (FFI)

The **Health and Safety (Fees) Regulations 2012** allow the HSE to recover its costs for carrying out its regulatory functions from those found to be in **material breach** of health and safety law.

A material breach is when, in the opinion of the HSE inspector, there is or has been a contravention of health and safety law that requires them to issue either:

- a notification of contravention (a letter that does not constitute formal enforcement action);
- an improvement or prohibition notice; or
- a prosecution.

The written notification must include the following information:

- the law that the inspector's opinion relates to;
- the reasons for their opinion; and
- notification that a fee is payable to HSE.

FFI applies where HSE is the enforcing authority. It does not apply to other health and safety enforcement authorities (such as local authorities). It only applies to legislation made under **HSWA**, (e.g. **MHSWR**).

The fee payable is based on the amount of time it takes HSE to identify and conclude its regulatory action in relation to the material breach (including associated office work). This is calculated using a standard hourly rate (currently £129 per hour). Material breaches discovered during a site visit would result in FFI being charged for the entire duration of that site visit.

Invoices are payable within 30 days. If a duty-holder disagrees with an invoice issued by HSE then they must:

- Query the invoice within 21 days of issue.
- Raise a dispute, in writing, within 21 days of the query reply, if they still disagree with the invoice.

Simple Cautions

The 'simple caution' procedure is used by some local authorities providing that the evidence available suggests that a conviction is more likely than an acquittal before a court, the offender admits the offence and agrees to be cautioned.

HSE enforcement officers tend to use alternative enforcement options available under the **HSWA**.

In Scotland, the Procurator Fiscal decides whether, in the particular case, a simple caution should be issued rather than taking legal proceedings.

Prosecution

Criminal prosecutions result in a trial heard in either the Magistrates' Court or the Crown Court (in England and Wales) or the Justice of the Peace or Sheriff Court (in Scotland). The case is brought by the enforcement agency itself in England and Wales, although in Scotland the Procurator Fiscal brings the case on behalf of the inspectors.

The particular court in which a case is held depends upon the type of offence and dictates the penalties which may be imposed.

There are three types of offence:

- Summary Offences

  These are minor offences which can be decided in a Magistrates' Court (England and Wales) or the Justice of the Peace Court or Summary Division of the Sheriff Court (in Scotland).

- Indictable Offences (Solemn Offences, in Scotland)

  These are the more serious types of offence. A formal document (the indictment) is drawn up following proceedings held in the Magistrates' Court (Sheriff Court in Scotland).

  The trial of indictable offences takes place before a judge (and jury) in the Crown Court in England and Wales, or, in Scotland, the Solemn Division of the Sheriff Court, or the High Court of Justiciary.

- Triable Either Way

  These are offences which may either be tried as summary offences in the Magistrates' Court or be heard by a judge and jury in the Crown Court. Most health and safety offences fall into this category.

  There are a number of reasons why a case may go to Crown Court:

  - The prosecution could seek for the case to be sent to the Crown Court due to its seriousness.
  - The magistrates could decide to send the case up to Crown Court for trial or sentencing.
  - The accused could request that the case goes to Crown Court so that they be heard by a judge and jury.

Penalties

The sentence imposed for a breach of health and safety law will depend on the specific offence and which court is involved. For most offences, the penalties are:

- **Magistrates' Court:**
  - unlimited fine and/or
  - 6 months' prison*.
- **Crown Court:**
  - unlimited fine and/or
  - 2 years' prison.

Similar penalties may be imposed by the equivalent courts in Scotland. These penalties are set out in the **Health and Safety (Offences) Act 2008* as modified by the Legal Aid, Sentencing and Punishment of Offenders Act 2012 (Fines on Summary Conviction) Regulations 2015**.

** The Health and Safety (Offences) Act 2008 appears to indicate a maximum prison sentence of 12 months at Magistrates' Court. However, the current maximum prison sentence that can be imposed by magistrates for any offence (not just health and safety) is 6 months.*

Criminal courts can make a compensation award to a person who has been injured or has suffered loss as a result of a criminal offence. This is in addition to any punishment from the Court. Criminal courts do not usually do this in health and safety cases where an employee is able to gain compensation by way of a civil action.

Defences

Where a prosecution is being brought under **HSWA**, the accused can defend themselves by arguing that, on balance of probabilities, they have done everything that was practicable or reasonably practicable in the circumstances.

Section 40 of **HSWA** reverses the normal burden of proof and standard of proof to put the onus on the accused to prove their innocence. If they had done all that was practicable or reasonably practicable under the circumstances, then this would be deemed an adequate defence to make. This, for example, could be done by demonstrating that an ACoP had been complied with. The standard of proof here is that the defendant must demonstrate their innocence on "the balance of probabilities".

This is different from most criminal cases, where there is a presumption of innocence and the prosecution must prove guilt "beyond all reasonable doubt".

Manslaughter

In very rare cases, organisations and/or individuals are charged with manslaughter (or homicide in Scotland) associated with a health and safety failure that has caused death. This is a very serious criminal offence:

- **Individuals** – can be charged with **gross negligence manslaughter** (or **culpable homicide** in Scotland), where their conduct fell well below the standards of a reasonable man and resulted in someone's death. This carries a maximum sentence of life imprisonment.
- **Organisations** – can be charged with **corporate manslaughter** (**corporate homicide** in Scotland). The penalty on conviction is an unlimited fine and the organisation may be ordered to publicise its offence and/or remedy its management failings.

Organisations can face a charge of corporate manslaughter associated with a health and safety failure

The **Corporate Manslaughter and Corporate Homicide Act 2007** has simplified the law on corporate manslaughter.

Under the Act, an organisation will be guilty of the offence if the way that the organisation managed or organised its activities:

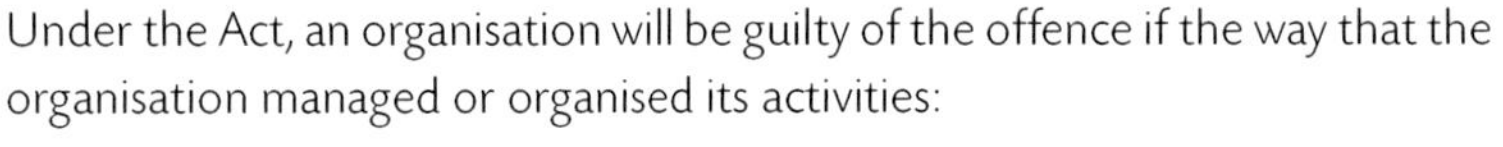

- caused a person's death;
- amounts to a gross breach of their duty of care to the deceased; **and**
- if the way in which the organisation is managed or organised by its senior management is a substantial element in the gross breach.

Note that in some cases individuals **and** organisations have been charged with offences under **HSWA and** with manslaughter and corporate manslaughter offences:

- The **individual** might be charged with a **HSWA** Section 7 offence (see later) and gross negligence manslaughter.
- The **organisation** might be charged with a **HSWA** Section 2 offence (see later) and corporate manslaughter.

Civil Law

Tort of Negligence

A tort is a civil wrong. The remedy for a tort is action through the civil courts. In Scotland, the word 'delict' is used instead.

Torts include civil wrongs such as defamation and trespass, but the one of particular interest in the context of health and safety is negligence.

Negligence can be simply defined as a failure to take reasonable care when a duty to do so existed.

If a person is injured or suffers some other form of loss as a result of someone else's negligence then they can use the civil legal system to claim compensation using the Tort of Negligence.

Common law has determined that we all owe each other a duty of care as we go about our daily lives, for example, when driving we owe a duty to all other road users. At work the employer owes a duty of care to their employees. Breach of this duty of care is what we call "negligence".

To demonstrate negligence the claimant must show that:

- **A duty of care was owed** to them by the defendant (the person or organisation that they are suing).
- This **duty of care was breached**.
- They suffered an **injury or loss as a direct result** of the breach of duty of care.

The claimant must prove their case on a balance of probabilities.

- Duty of Care

  The concept of a "duty of care" stems from common law and the case of ***Donoghue v. Stevenson (1932)***. This case involved a woman consuming a soft drink in which was found the remains of a decomposed snail. She was subsequently ill and sued the manufacturer. In the judgment, it was held that reasonable care must be taken to avoid acts or omissions which, with reasonable foresight, you would know would be likely to injure your neighbour. This is known as the **neighbour principle**.

  In other words, you owe a duty of care to your neighbours, i.e. to the people who it is reasonably foreseeable that your acts or omissions might harm.

- Breach of Duty

  This has nothing to do with a breach of statute law. Instead the question is whether the defendant behaved in a **reasonable** manner. The breach of duty might be by **act** or by **omission**. Did the defendant act in a way that a reasonable person might be expected to act in the circumstances? Or did they fail to do something that a reasonable person might be expected to do in the circumstances?

- Injury as a Direct Result

  The injury or loss must have arisen directly from the breach of duty of care and the claimant will have to demonstrate this. For example, failure to support the sides of an excavation (breach) leads to the collapse of the excavation, which in turn leads to crush injuries to the worker in the excavation.

Defences Against Tort of Negligence

The three proofs for negligence give rise to the **defences** that might be used by the defendant:

- **No duty of care owed** – the defendant did not owe a duty of care to the claimant so did not have to have them in mind as they went about their activities.

- **Duty of care not breached** – the defendant did everything that a reasonable person might have done in the circumstances.
- **No injury or loss as a direct result of the breach** – the nature of the injury or loss cannot be substantiated, or it has occurred but cannot be linked directly to the breach of duty by the defendant.

There are other defences available such as:

- *Volenti non fit injuria* – the idea that the claimant was a willing volunteer and accepted the risk of personal injury when taking part in the activity. This defence cannot be used by an employer to defend a claim from his employees.
- **Contributory negligence** – see below.
- The facts of the case are disputed, for example, the event didn't happen.
- The **Social Action, Responsibility and Heroism Act 2015 (SARAH)** effectively creates possible additional defences in a civil court of law. Put simply, where negligence is alleged, the court needs to take account of whether the person was acting either to benefit society/individuals, acting responsibly or acting heroically. These tests have not yet entered into legal force as the law is new, but an example where it could be used is as a defence for a first aider being sued for causing injury while carrying out treatment which was within their training and skills.

Contributory Negligence

Contributory negligence is a partial defence against a claim of negligence where **a part of the blame for the injury is attributed to someone else** other than the defendant. In many cases it is used as a way of passing some of the blame for the injury to the claimant. Other parties might also be held responsible.

For example, if an employee fails to comply with their training, fails to use the personal protective equipment (PPE) that has been provided and fails to heed warning signs, they might receive an injury. If that employee can then demonstrate that there was a complete failure to provide adequate supervision in the workplace (which would have ensured that they used the PPE) then they may be able to claim compensation for their injury.

The employer might admit partial liability for the injury because they failed to provide adequate supervision. But the employer might also claim contributory negligence because the employee had been trained, provided with PPE and warning signs were in place. If the judge accepts this argument they will award damages on a pro-rata basis depending on where they see the blame being apportioned.

Vicarious Liability

Vicarious liability is the simple idea that **an employer can be held liable for the negligent acts (or omissions) of his employees**. So, if an employee is negligent and injures another person, then that injured person can claim compensation through the civil legal system from the employer (rather than having to sue the individual employee who actually caused their injury).

So, for example, if an untrained, unauthorised driver runs over a member of the public whilst trying to move a loaded pallet with a forklift truck, the injured member of the public can sue the employer for their injury.

The main restriction on vicarious liability is that the employee has to be acting in the course of employment when they commit their negligent act. If they were not working when they caused the injury, then they can be held personally liable and their employer can escape liability.

Tort of Breach of Statutory Duty

Health and safety legislation **cannot** be used to give a right of civil action in almost all circumstances. In other words, injured employees and other people cannot sue employers or others that they hold responsible for their injuries using breaches of health and safety legislation as the basis for their claim. This is because Section 47 of **HSWA** explicitly prevents the Act or Regulations made under the Act from being used for this purpose. The Act and Regulations are said to be '**statut**e barred'.

However, there is one exception to this statute bar and that concerns new and expectant mothers. Where a new or expectant mother suffers harm as a result of her employer's failure to carry out a risk assessment and/or make suitable arrangements to protect her health and safety (as required by regulations 16 and 17 of **MHSWR**) then she has the right to sue her employer for that harm using tort of breach of statutory duty. **MHSWR** and new and expectant mothers are dealt with in more detail later in this element.

Compensation

The compensation awarded to a successful claimant is intended to return the claimant to the position that they were in before the injury occurred. Whilst the court cannot repair the damage of an injury, they can award money to compensate for that injury. The compensation awarded is split into two categories:

- **General damages** – for pain and suffering, loss of amenity, loss of future earnings, etc. These amounts are for the court to quantify.
- **Special damages** – for loss of earning up to the trial date, travel expense to hospital, etc. These amounts have to be quantified and proven by the claimant.

So, the amount of compensation awarded is directly determined by how much pain and suffering was caused by the event and by any treatment or rehabilitation that followed, how much loss of amenity (enjoyment of hobbies, pastimes, etc.) has been caused and how the injury has impacted on the person's financial situation and their ability to earn a living.

Employment Tribunals

Employment tribunals are not involved in determining compensation for work-related injuries.

They are, however, responsible for settling disputes that arise out of employment law, such as cases on:

- Unfair and constructive dismissal.
- Sex, race and age discrimination.

In the context of health and safety law, Employment tribunals are important for two reasons:

- They hear appeals against enforcement notices.
- They hear appeals from Safety Representatives whose rights have been withheld.

Employment tribunals provide a cheaper, less formal way to resolve disputes without recourse to the courts. There is a link from tribunals into the civil legal system.

DEFINITION

SAFETY REPRESENTATIVES

Individuals appointed by a recognised trade union whose role is to represent a group of workers. They have certain rights and entitlements in law in the UK.

STUDY QUESTIONS

6. What is the legal status of:
    (a) Regulations?
    (b) Approved Codes of Practice?
    (c) HSE Guidance Notes?
7. What is the difference between the civil and criminal law in respect of:
    (a) The remedy sought?
    (b) The burden and standard of proof?
    (c) Who starts the legal action?
8. Explain the principle of judicial precedent.
9. What is delegated legislation?
10. What are the common law duties of employers?
11. What is the difference between an Improvement Notice and a Prohibition Notice?
12. Does an appeal against an Enforcement Notice suspend the Notice?
13. What role do employment tribunals have in health and safety?
14. What are the tests of negligence?
15. What is the relationship of the health and safety regulations to **HSWA**?
16. What are the two main enforcement agencies for health and safety under **HSWA** in the UK?
17. Identify four powers of inspectors under Section 20 of **HSWA**.

(Suggested Answers are at the end.)

The Health and Safety at Work, Etc. Act 1974

IN THIS SECTION...

- The **Health and Safety at Work, etc. Act 1974** is the principal piece of statute law regulating health and safety in workplaces. The Act creates duty holders and identifies who they owe a duty towards.
- The employer owes a duty to his employees to ensure, so far as is reasonably practicable, their health, safety and welfare at work.
- 'So far as is reasonably practicable' is a key phrase meaning that a balance must be struck between the level of risk and the cost, measured in time, money and effort, of reducing that risk.
- An employer also owes a duty to ensure the health and safety of non-employees.
- People who control premises used as workplaces (such as office landlords) have a duty to the people using those premises.
- Designers and manufacturers of articles or substances used at work have a duty to the end users.
- Employees have a duty to themselves and others and must co-operate with their employer.
- The Act also prohibits anyone from misusing safety equipment and prohibits employers from charging employees for things done to achieve legal compliance.
- Directors, senior managers and external advisers can be charged with offences committed by an organisation.

Scope

The **Health and Safety at Work, etc. Act 1974** (**HSWA**) covers all workplaces and all work activities in Great Britain. In Northern Ireland, the **Health and Safety at Work (Northern Ireland) Order 1978** achieves the same end.

The Act is very general in its coverage and flexible in terms of interpretation. Rather than focusing on fine detail and being prescriptive about exactly what must be done in specific workplaces, it takes a broad view. It recognises that many different parties influence standards of health and safety in workplaces and it then assigns duties to those parties (making them **duty holders**). No specific detail is given to each duty holder about exactly what they must do to achieve compliance. Instead, each duty holder is given some general aims to achieve. In this way, the Act is an example of '**goal-setting**' legislation rather than 'prescriptive' legislation.

HSWA - the principal law regulating health and safety

The Act is made up of over 80 sections. In the following pages, the key sections of the Act are outlined (Sections 2 - 9 and Sections 36 and 37) and the duty holders and their duties are identified.

The Employer's Duty to His Employees

Section 2 of the Act states the duties of the employer towards his employees. This section is broken down into a number of sub-sections.

Section 2(1)

Section 2(1) states the **general duties of the employer towards his employees**:

"to ensure, so far as is reasonably practicable, the health, safety and welfare at work of all his employees".

This general duty is worth examining in more detail:

- The duty holder is the employer.
- They owe the duty only to their employees.
- They must ensure health, safety and welfare. (These three things have been defined earlier in this element.)
- The employer does not have to ensure absolute health or absolute safety. This would require that the employer provided a workplace free of all risk, (i.e. a zero-risk environment). Instead, the employer's duty is qualified by the phrase "**so far as is reasonably practicable**". This is a key phrase.

So Far As Is Reasonably Practicable

As mentioned above, the employer is not required to provide a risk-free or zero-risk workplace. Such an environment does not (and cannot) exist. There is risk associated with all places and activities in life. Even simple tasks such as putting on clothes involves an element of risk to safety (the number of people visiting the Accident and Emergency department at their local hospital because of injuries sustained when getting dressed in the morning is quite surprising!). Similarly, everyone is exposed to health risk all of the time, (e.g. exposure to background radiation, which is always present in all locations, increases the risk of cancer).

Therefore, the employer's duty is **qualified** by the phrase "so far as is reasonably practicable". This phrase has been defined by case law.

TOPIC FOCUS

So Far As Is Reasonably Practicable

This means that the duty holder must assess the **degree of risk** against the **sacrifice** involved in introducing control measures to eliminate or control the risk. This sacrifice can be measured in terms of **financial cost**, **time** and **effort**.

If it can be shown that there is gross disproportion between the risk and the sacrifice then the sacrifice does not have to be made.

So, for example, no-one worries about the risk of paper cuts in an office environment because the risk is trivial compared to the difficulty of eliminating or controlling the risk (what could you do – make all office workers wear cut-resistant gloves?). But employers do have to avert the risk of falls from height when workers are fixing the roof to a large steel frame building because the risks are clearly very high. Therefore, a lot of time, trouble and money has to be dedicated to controlling this risk.

Illustration of 'Reasonably Practicable'

Shall and Practicable

There are two other important phrases that are used to impose a duty in statute law: "shall" and "so far as is practicable".

TOPIC FOCUS

Shall **– an "absolute" duty**

When the word 'shall' is used in statute law it creates an absolute duty. This means that the requirement must be met and there is no acceptable excuse for not doing so.

Practicable

When the phrase 'so far as is practicable' is used in statute law it means that the duty must be complied with to the extent that it is possible to do so in the light of current knowledge and invention. So if it is possible then it must be done (irrespective of cost). If it is not possible then it does not have to be done.

Section 2(2)

Section 2(2) states the **specific duties** of the **employer** to his employees. It adds a little more detail to flesh out what the employer must do. Each requirement is qualified by the phase "so far as is reasonably practicable".

TOPIC FOCUS

The **employer's specific duties to his employees** are to provide so far as is reasonably practicable:

2(2)(a) Safe plant and systems of work.

2(2)(b) Safe use, handling, storage and transport of articles and substances.

2(2)(c) Information, instruction, training and supervision.

2(2)(d) A safe workplace and safe access to it and egress from it.

2(2)(e) A safe working environment with adequate welfare facilities.

Note that the above is an abbreviation of the wording of the Act.

This section does not provide any detail for the employer on exactly how to achieve these ends. For that, the employer has to turn to the regulations and their accompanying Approved Codes of Practice and Guidance. For example, requirement 2(2)(b) - to provide safe use, handling, storage and transport of articles and substances - does not state exactly what should be done when handling hazardous substances such as industrial chemicals. But the **Control of Substances Hazardous to Health Regulations 2002** and their accompanying ACoP and guidance do give very clear indications of what must be done to ensure safety.

Section 2(3)-2(7)

- **Section 2(3)** requires an employer to prepare a **written health and safety policy** that will include a general statement of policy and the organisation and arrangements for carrying it out. This policy must be revised as necessary and brought to the attention of employees.

  Subsequent legislation has made a written policy a legal requirement where the employer has five or more employees.

- **Section 2(4)** concerns the **appointment of safety representatives** by recognised trade unions.
- **Section 2(6)** requires employers to **consult with safety representatives**.
- **Section 2(7)** requires employers to establish a **safety committee**.

These last three sections will be examined in more detail in Element 3.

The Employer's Duty to Others

Section 3 places a duty on employers to ensure, so far as is reasonably practicable, that non-employees are not exposed to risks to their health and safety.

- The duty holder is the employer.
- They owe the duty to everyone else who is not an employee (clients, visitors, contractors, the public, etc.).
- They must ensure health and safety.
- The duty is qualified by "so far as is reasonably practicable".

Section 3 also places the same duty on many **self-employed** people. They must carry out their work so that they do not create risk to themselves or others. The **Deregulation Act 2015** exempts some self-employed people from Section 3 of **HSWA**. However, self-employed people engaged in a 'prescribed' undertaking such as construction or agricultural work still fall under Section 3 of **HSWA,** as do any self-employed people whose work creates significant risk for others (such as safety consultants).

Controllers of Premises

Section 4 imposes duties on those who have some degree of **control over non-domestic premises** that they are making available for others (non-employees) to use as workplaces or for work activities. These persons can be referred to as 'controllers of premises'. A typical example would be a landlord or commercial property management company that owns and rents an office block for various other companies to occupy.

The controller of premises' duties are to ensure, so far as is reasonably practicable, that:

- The premises are safe.
- The means of access and egress are safe.
- Any plant or substances provided by them for use in that premises are safe.

Designers', Manufacturers', Importers' and Suppliers' Duties

Section 6 details the duties on any person who **designs**, **manufactures**, **imports** or **supplies** any article or substance for use at work.

These duty holders must ensure that:

- So far as is reasonably practicable, articles are designed and constructed to be safe and without risk to health at all times when they are being set, cleaned, used and maintained.
- Substances are likewise safe and without risk to health when being used, handled, stored or transported.
- Testing and examination is carried out to ensure the required level of safety and freedom from risk.
- Employers are provided with information on the safe use, dismantling and disposal of the articles and substances.
- Employers are given revised information should a subsequent serious risk become known.

Employee's Duties

TOPIC FOCUS

Section 7 of the Act states that it shall be the duty of every **employee** to:

- Take **reasonable care** for the health and safety of **himself** and of **other persons** who may be affected by his **acts or omissions** at work.
- **Co-operate** with the **employer** to enable compliance with legal requirements.

Interference and Misuse

Section 8 states that no person shall intentionally or recklessly **interfere with or misuse** anything provided in the interests of health, safety or welfare in pursuance of legal requirements.

The expression 'no person' implies that the duty is not limited to employees.

Free of Charge to Employees

Section 9 states that **the employer cannot charge** his employee for things done to achieve legal compliance. (Note that this prohibition on charging has many caveats.)

Offences Due to Fault of Others

Section 36 states that where an offence committed by a company is due to the act or default of some other person, (e.g. advice from a consultant or safety officer), that other person (consultant or safety officer) may be charged with and convicted of the offence (whether or not proceedings are taken against the company itself).

Personal Liability of Directors and Senior Managers

Section 37 states that directors and senior managers of a company, **as well as** the company itself (body corporate), may be **personally liable** for breaches of the law. Directors and senior managers can be prosecuted for offences committed by the company if it can be shown that they consented, connived or were negligent in their duties in allowing the offence to be committed.

MORE...

www.

The full version of **HSWA** can be obtained from www.legislation.gov.uk but you do not need to know it all for this course, and some sections have been removed so are no longer relevant, e.g. Section 5.

STUDY QUESTIONS

18. What is the difference between an absolute duty and a qualified duty, and how may the duty be qualified?
19. State the general duties of employers to employees under Section 2 of the **Health and Safety at Work, etc. Act 1974**.
20. Explain the meaning of the phrase "so far as is reasonably practicable".
21. State the duties of employees under the **Health and Safety at Work, etc. Act 1974**.

(Suggested Answers are at the end.)

The Management of Health and Safety at Work Regulations 1999

IN THIS SECTION...

- The **Management of Health and Safety at Work Regulations 1999** place various duties on an employer.
- Foremost amongst these is the requirement to carry out a suitable and sufficient risk assessment.
- The employer must also make arrangements for health and safety management; develop procedures to deal with imminent danger; provide health surveillance, information and training to employees; provide information to other employers and co-operate and co-ordinate with those who share their premises.
- Employees are also given duties.
- New and expectant mothers, and young people are identified as two vulnerable groups who have to be given a higher level of protection through the risk assessment process.

Scope

The **Management of Health and Safety at Work Regulations 1999** (**MHSWR**) cover the same geographic area as **HSWA** and cover all workplaces and work activities. They contain more specific and detailed requirements; in particular, about risk assessment and management issues, such as the provision of training and information. In effect, they add detail to certain parts of the framework created by **HSWA**.

HINTS AND TIPS

Note that in the following section, regulation numbers are given in brackets after each requirement. These regulation numbers do not need to be remembered for exam purposes; they are simply included to allow cross-referencing back to original text if necessary.

The Employer's Duties

Most duties contained in **MHSWR** fall on the employer.

Risk Assessment (Reg. 3)

- The employer shall make a suitable and sufficient assessment of the risks to both his employees and non-employees.
- The assessment must be recorded if the employer has five or more employees.
- The assessment must be reviewed.

Risk assessment will be examined in detail in Element 3.

Note that it states in **MHSWR** that an employer shall carry out a suitable and sufficient risk assessment, the regulations make it an **absolute** duty for the employer to comply.

Risks need to be assessed by someone competent

Principles of Prevention to be Applied (Reg. 4)

- In implementing any preventive and protective measures, the employer must do so on the basis of some principles of prevention listed in Schedule 1 to **MHSWR**.
- This Schedule is, in effect, an appendix to the regulations and has full legal status.

The principles of prevention will be examined in detail in Element 3.

Health and Safety Arrangements (Reg. 5)

- The employer must make arrangements for the effective planning, organisation, control, monitoring and review of the preventive and protective measures.
- These arrangements must be recorded where the employer has five or more employees.

The concepts of safety management systems and safety policies both relate to this regulation and will be examined in detail in Element 2.

Health Surveillance (Reg. 6)

- The employer must ensure that employees are provided with appropriate health surveillance.

Health surveillance is usually a legal requirement of the regulations governing specific hazards. For example, audiometry is a legal requirement under the **Control of Noise at Work Regulations 2005**. The health surveillance requirements for various hazards are discussed later.

DEFINITION 

AUDIOMETRY

A test of a person's hearing level carried out by measuring their response to sounds played through headphones, usually in a soundproof enclosure. It is carried out by a competent technician or nurse.

Health and Safety Assistance (Reg. 7)

- The employer must appoint one or more **competent persons** to assist him in undertaking the measures he needs to take to comply with health and safety law.
- A competent person is someone with sufficient **training** and **experience** or **knowledge** and other qualities to enable him to give proper assistance.

Procedures for Serious and Imminent Danger and Contact with External Services (Regs 8 and 9)

- The employer must develop procedures to be implemented in the event of **serious and imminent danger**.
- They must nominate a sufficient number of competent persons to implement these procedures.
- They must ensure that any necessary **contacts** with external services are arranged, such as first aid, emergency medical care and rescue work.
- Employees should be prevented from going into dangerous areas. Where the employer needs to restrict access for health and safety reasons, only those who are suitably trained should be allowed to go into the areas e.g. a high hazard laboratory may have a coded lock.

Information for Employees (Reg. 10)

The employer must provide his employees with comprehensible and relevant **information** on:

(a) The risks to their health and safety.

(b) Preventive control measures.

(c) Emergency procedures.

Co-operation and Co-ordination where Two or More Employers Share a Workplace (Reg. 11)

Where two or more employers share a workplace, each employer must:

- **Co-operate and co-ordinate** with the other employers to ensure health and safety.
- **Inform** the other employers of the risks to their employees' health and safety arising from his undertaking.

TOPIC FOCUS

Factors that should be considered to ensure co-ordination and co-operation when employers are sharing a workplace include:

- Specific hazards and risks arising from each employer's activities.
- Security and site access control.
- Site speed limits and traffic rules.
- Maintenance of shared areas and corridors.
- Emergency procedures.
- First aid facilities and first aiders.
- Heating, lighting and ventilation maintenance.
- Traffic routes and standards.

Information for Other Workers (Regs 12 and 15)

- The employer must provide other workers (who are not his employees) with **information** on the risks to their health and safety and preventive control measures.

  This means that contractors working on an employer's premises must be provided with essential health and safety information.

- Workers on temporary contracts must be provided with information about any specific qualification and health surveillance requirements.

Capabilities and Training (Reg. 13)

- The employer must take into account the capabilities of employees when allocating tasks.
- The employer must provide adequate **health and safety training** when employees are:
  - First recruited.
  - Exposed to new or increased risks.
- Training should be repeated periodically where appropriate and should take place during working hours.

Employees' Duties (Reg. 14)

The **MHSWR** expand upon the general duties placed on **employees** by **HSWA.**

TOPIC FOCUS

Employees must:

- Use equipment and materials in accordance with any instruction and training given.
- Inform the employer of any work situation that represents serious and immediate danger to health and safety or any shortcomings in the employer's arrangements for health and safety.

Protection of New and Expectant Mothers (Regs 16-18)

Where work could present a risk to new or expectant mothers, a risk assessment must consider this.

- Where a risk cannot be avoided, the employer must alter working conditions and hours to avoid the risk.
- Where this would not avoid the risk, the employer must suspend the worker on full pay.
- The employer may have to suspend a night-shift worker if notified by a medical practitioner.
- The employer does not have to take any of the above preventive actions until notified in writing about the employee's status.

The specific hazards that present risk to new and expectant mothers are described in Element 3.

DEFINITION

NEW MOTHER

A woman who has just given birth, up to 6 months after the birth, or while still breastfeeding. An expectant mother is a pregnant woman.

EXPECTANT MOTHER

A pregnant woman.

Protection of Young Persons (Reg. 19)

- The employer must ensure that young persons at work are protected from any risks to their health or safety.
- The specific characteristics that put a young person more at risk are:
  - Their lack of experience.
  - Their poor perception of risk.
  - Their physical and mental immaturity.

The protection measures appropriate for young persons are outlined in Element 3.

DEFINITION

YOUNG PERSONS

Defined in **MHSWR** as anyone under the age of 18.

STUDY QUESTIONS

22. State the legal duty for recording risk assessments.

23. What specific types of procedure must the employer develop under **MHSWR**?

24. Define a 'young person'.

(Suggested Answers are at the end.)

Contractor Management

IN THIS SECTION...

- When a client takes on the services of a contractor both parties have shared responsibilities for ensuring good standards of health and safety.
- The client must carefully select contractors on the basis of their health and safety competence. This can be done by looking at the contractors' policy documents, accident and enforcement history, references, qualifications and experience.
- The client must ensure that contractors carry out risk assessments and develop method statements for their work. The client must monitor contractors to ensure that they work safely to agreed methods.
- The **Construction (Design and Management) Regulations 2015 (CDM)** impose a framework for the management of construction projects (both non-domestic and domestic). For projects involving more than one contractor, the **CDM Regulations** identify six duty holders who each have specific duties assigned to them: the client, principal designer, designers, principal contractor, contractors and workers.
- The regulations require the preparation of a Construction Phase Plan and, where the project involves more than one contractor, a Health and Safety File for the finished structure.
- Projects over 30 working days in duration **and** involving more than 20 workers at any one time, **or** involving over 500 worker days must be notified to the HSE by the client.

Introduction

Contractors are used widely in the workplace, either to deliver a specific project or skill or to deliver extra labour when needed. For example, a site wanting to extend the premises would usually take on a building contractor to deliver the project rather than employing the manpower directly, in the same way a company may engage a training contractor to deliver a NEBOSH course.

The Client/Contractor Relationship

Contractors are engaged by clients in lots of different circumstances at work. A contractor may be engaged to perform a one-off service, such as the refitting of an IT suite, or they may be engaged on a more permanent basis to provide in-house catering or cleaning services.

Quite clearly it is not in the interest of health and safety for the client to ignore the risks associated with the contractor's work or for the contractor to ignore the risks inherent in the client's workplace.

This section outlines some simple principles for the management of the contractor/client relationship. It then moves on to the specific issue of the management of construction projects under the **Construction (Design and Management) Regulations 2015 (CDM)**.

DEFINITION

CONTRACTOR AND CLIENT

Contractor – a person or organisation engaged to undertake certain work on behalf of a client but not under the client's direct supervision and control.

Client – a person or organisation who engages a contractor.

Shared Duties

Contractors are responsible for their own health and safety and the health and safety of others who might be affected by their work activities.

A **contractor company** (such as a cleaning company) is an **employer** in their own right. They therefore, as noted earlier in the section on **HSWA**, owe a duty to:

- Their employees (the individual contract cleaners doing the work in a client's premises) because of Section 2.
- Other people (such as the client's employees and visitors to the client's premises) who might be affected by their work, because of Section 3.

And the **individual cleaners** doing the work in the client's premises are **employees** of the contract cleaning company. They therefore owe a duty to:

- themselves; and
- other people (such as fellow workers, the client's employees and visitors to the client's premises) who might be affected by their acts and omissions, because of Section 7.

The **client** (as an **employer**) owes a duty to:

- His own employees because of Section 2.
- Others who might be affected by his undertaking because of Section 3.

  These others would include:

  - The contract cleaners in the premises.
  - Any other workers in the premises (such as other contractors).
  - Visitors to the client's premises.

Importantly, case law exists which clearly indicates that when a client brings a contractor onto site the contractor's work becomes a part of the client's undertaking.

The individual **employees** of the **client** also owe a duty to:

- themselves; and
- other people (such as contract cleaners, fellow employees, visitors) who might be affected by their acts or omissions because of Section 7.

Put simply, the contractor and his employees owe a duty to everyone and the client and his employees also owe a duty to everyone.

There are additional duties under **MHSWR** to carry out risk assessment, provide information and training, etc.

The responsibility for ensuring health and safety is therefore **shared** between the client and the contractor. It is in both parties' interests to ensure that each does everything that might be considered **reasonable** in the circumstances to discharge their duty and avoid criminal liability.

The way that a client manages contractors can be broken down into three key areas:

- Selecting the contractor.
- Planning the work.
- Monitoring the work.

The Selection of Contractors

TOPIC FOCUS

Selecting the Contractor

It is good practice to select a contractor carefully on the basis of their health and safety competence. To help in this, you can ask to see evidence of competence, such as:

- A copy of their health and safety policy.
- Examples of risk assessments.
- The qualifications and training records of staff.
- Membership of a professional organisation or certified body.
- Records of maintenance and testing for plant and equipment.
- Names of previous or current clients.
- Accident history records.
- Records of enforcement action taken by authorities against them.
- Proof of adequate resources, such as access to specialist safety advice.
- Proof of adequate insurance.

Planning and Control of Contractors

Planning the Work

Information must be exchanged between the client and the contractor. The client should tell the contractor about the hazards and risks in the workplace, and the contractor should tell the client about the hazards and risks created by the contract work. In this way, the work can be planned so that everyone is kept safe.

The contractor should carry out risk assessments on the work involved and develop safe working methods to control the risks identified. This safe working method must be documented and is often referred to as a "method statement".

Monitoring the Work

Arrangements must be made by the client to ensure the contractor complies with safe working practices. These arrangements should include:

- Having a signing in and out procedure.
- Ensuring that the contractor provides a named works foreman.
- Carrying out site induction training for all contractor workers.
- Controlling high-risk activities with a permit-to-work system.

The client will need to monitor the contractor's work to ensure that the contractor is working to agreed safety standards. This can be done by monitoring against the method statement that was developed during the planning stage.

DEFINITION 

PERMIT-TO-WORK

A formal, documented safety procedure forming part of a safe system of work, which ensures that all necessary actions are taken before, during and after particularly high-risk work. We will cover permits in more detail in Element 3.

Management of Construction Projects

Construction projects usually involve many different parties in a collaborative effort. Each party has a role to play in ensuring that the project is carried out safely and that the end result (the structure) is safe.

All construction projects are subject to the **Construction (Design and Management) Regulations 2015 (CDM)**. These regulations are split into various parts, some of which deal with the practical control of construction work. The following section deals with projects involving more than one contractor where all parts of the regulations apply. (Note that reference to 'more than one contractor' refers to more than one contractor organisation, not more than one individual worker.)

Notification

A notifiable project is one where the construction phase is planned to:

- last over 30 working days **and** involve more than 20 workers at any one time; **or**
- involve more than 500 worker days.

If a project falls into one or both of these categories, then a notification has to be sent by the client to the HSE, detailing:

- The address of the construction site.
- Brief description of project and construction work involved.
- Contact details of the client.
- Contact details of the principal designer.
- Contact details of the principal contractor.
- Planned date for the start of the construction phase and its planned duration.
- Time allowed for planning and preparation for construction work.
- Estimated maximum number of people at work on the site.

CDM Duty Holders

For projects involving more than one contractor, the **CDM Regulations** identify six duty holders who have a part to play in ensuring safety:

- The **client** - for whom the project is being carried out (this can be commercial or domestic). The client has health and safety responsibility at the tender stage.
- The **principal designer (PD)** - who plans and co-ordinates health and safety in the pre-construction phase of the project. The PD has health and safety responsibility through the pre-construction phase.
- **Designers** - who work under the control of the **principal designer**.

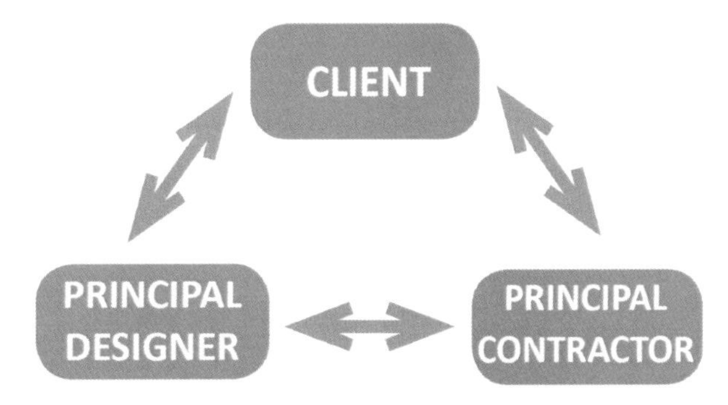

- The **principal contractor (PC)** - who plans and co-ordinates health and safety during the construction phase of the project. The PC takes health and safety responsibility through the construction phase.
- **Contractors** - who work under the control of the **principal contractor**.
- **Workers** - who undertake the construction work.

The regulations also require the preparation of a '**Construction Phase Plan**' for all construction work and a '**Health and Safety File**' for the finished structure if the construction work involved more than one contractor.

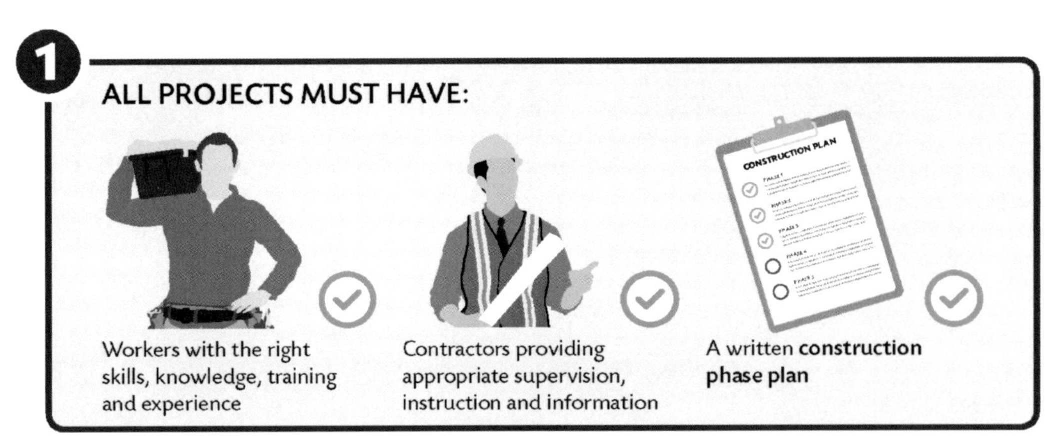

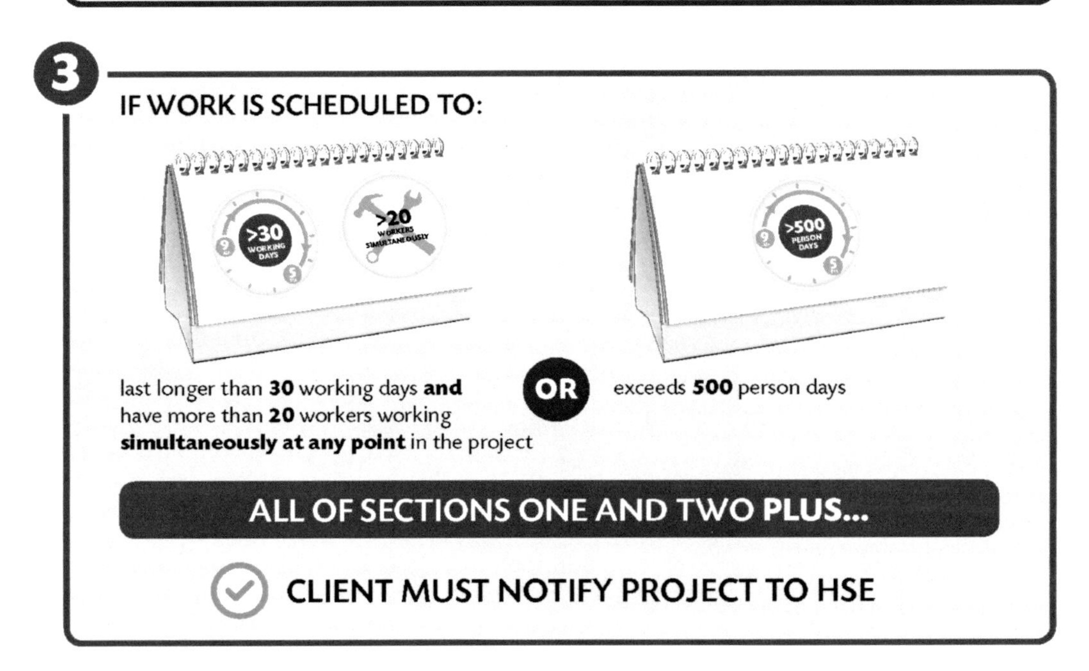

CDM requirements

The regulations assign the following duties to each party:

- The **client** should ensure that:
  - Suitably competent designers and contractors are appointed.
  - Adequate pre-construction information is provided to the other duty holders.
  - Principal designers and principal contractors carry out their duties.
  - A Construction Phase Plan for the project is prepared by the principal contractor before work starts.
  - The Health and Safety File is prepared by the principal designer for the building/structure and that this is made available for future reference.
  - Suitable welfare facilities are available during the construction phase.
  - Notifiable projects are notified to the HSE.

CDM applies to all construction work carried out for both commercial and domestic clients. However, for domestic clients, the clients' duties pass to the contractor or principal contractor (or principal designer where a written agreement has been entered into).

- **Designers** should ensure that:
  - The client is aware of his duties under the **CDM Regulations**.
  - Their design eliminates or minimises health and safety risks created by the project.
  - Design information is passed to the principal designer, client and contractors.
  - They communicate, co-operate and co-ordinate with other designers and contractors.
- The **principal designer** should ensure that:
  - They plan, manage, monitor and co-ordinate health and safety during the pre-construction phase of the project.
  - The client is advised on the bringing together of pre-construction information that will be useful to designers and contractors.
  - The design eliminates or minimises health and safety risks created by the project.
  - Proper communication, co-operation and co-ordination takes place during the pre-construction phase.
  - The Health and Safety File is prepared and passed to the client at the end of the project.
- The **principal contractor** should ensure that:
  - The construction phase of the project is adequately planned, managed, monitored and co-ordinated.
  - A Construction Phase Plan for the project exists and is kept up to date.
  - The site is secure.
  - All workers have access to suitable welfare facilities.
  - All contractors receive site-specific induction training.
  - Workers are consulted on site health and safety issues.
- **Contractors** should ensure that:
  - The client is aware of his duties under the **CDM Regulations**.
  - They plan, manage and monitor their own work to control safety risks.
  - Their workers have the skills, knowledge, training and experience to carry out their work safely.
  - They provide appropriate information, instruction and supervision to their workers.
- **Workers** should ensure that they:
  - Take reasonable care of their own health and safety and the health and safety of others who their work might affect.

Designers and main contractors must assess the safety implications of any changes to the design – both for construction workers and for end-users.

- Report anything that they see that could affect their own or others' health and safety.
- Co-operate with all other duty holders.

The Construction Phase Plan

The Construction Phase Plan is the health and safety management plan for the construction phase of the project.

The plan is the responsibility of the principal contractor (or contractor if the project involves only one contractor).

Typical contents would include:

1. **Project description:**
   - Including key project team members.
2. **Management of the work:**
   - Site rules.
   - Arrangements for ensuring co-operation between parties.
   - Arrangements for consultation.
   - Site induction.
   - Welfare facilities.
   - Fire and emergency procedures.
3. **Arrangements for controlling significant site risks:**
   - Safety risks, such as fall prevention.
   - Health risks, such as removal of asbestos.

The Health and Safety File

The Health and Safety File contains information about the new or modified structure that the client needs to know.

Typical content would include:

- Brief description of work.
- Residual hazards.
- Key structural principles.
- Hazardous material used.
- Information relevant to dismantling.
- Information on cleaning or maintenance equipment.
- Nature, location and marking of significant services.
- Information and as-built drawings of the structure and plant and equipment.

This file is created by the principal designer and passed to the client on completion of the project. The client must then keep the file up to date and make it available to workers who need to know its contents (such as future contractors).

STUDY QUESTIONS

25. List the criteria that might be used to assess the suitability of a contractor to undertake work on behalf of a client.
26. What types of construction project are notifiable projects?
27. What are the main duties of the following parties under the **CDM Regulations**?

    (a) The client.

    (b) The principal designer.

    (c) The principal contractor.

(Suggested Answers are at the end.)

Summary

This element has dealt with some of the basic principles of workplace health and safety.

In particular, this element has:

- Explained that health and safety is a multi-disciplinary topic that requires knowledge across a wide range of subjects and that there are barriers to the raising of health and safety standards in a workplace.
- Introduced some of the key words and phrases that will be used throughout this course, such as health, safety and welfare.
- Highlighted the three main reasons why an organisation has to manage health and safety, which can be summarised as moral, economic and legal.
- Identified some of the direct and indirect costs associated with accidents and ill health, some of which will be uninsured.
- Examined the framework created by the criminal and civil legal systems and the characteristics of both types of law.
- Outlined the two sources of law as statute law, made by Parliament, and common law, made by judges.
- Outlined the structure and hierarchy of the criminal and civil courts.
- Described the powers of HSE inspectors under **HSWA**, the characteristics of Improvement and Prohibition Notices they might issue, the principles of FFI and the penalties for breaching the Act.
- Explained the basic principles of the civil legal system, such as vicarious liability, the proofs required for Tort of Negligence and the defences available, such as contributory negligence.
- Examined the key sections of **HSWA** such as the Section 2 duty owed by an employer to his employees to ensure, so far as is reasonably practicable, their health, safety and welfare at work.
- Outlined the meaning of the phrase "so far as is reasonably practicable".
- Outlined the other duty holders identified in the Act, such as the self-employed, controllers of premises, designers and manufacturers, and employees.
- Outlined the liability of directors, senior managers and external advisers for offences committed by an organisation.
- Identified the key legal requirements of the **MHSWR**, in particular the requirement for the employer to carry out a suitable and sufficient risk assessment.
- Identified new and expectant mothers and young people as two vulnerable groups who are given special mention in **MHSWR**.
- Explained the shared responsibilities that exist when work is carried out by contractors for a client.
- Outlined a basic framework for the selection, monitoring and control of contractors by clients.
- Described how the **CDM Regulations** impose a framework for the management of construction projects; the six duty holders identified for projects involving more than one contractor; and the requirements to prepare a Construction Phase Plan, a Health and Safety File and notify of larger projects.

Exam Skills

Introduction

To pass the NEBOSH Certificate you need to perform well during the exams. You only have two hours and your performance will be related to two key factors:

- the amount that you can remember about the elements you've studied; and
- your success in applying that knowledge to an exam situation.

Being good at both aspects is essential. Being calm under exam pressure is pointless if you do not have a good knowledge of the information required to answer the exam questions.

Here we will consider some practical guidelines that can be used to increase success in the exam. Then you will find Exam Skills questions for you to answer at the end of each element, starting with this one.

Exam Requirements

The NGC1 exam consists of two sections:

- Section 1 contains one question which is likely to consist of a number of sub-parts. This question in total is worth 20 marks.
- Section 2 contains ten questions with each question being worth eight marks.

There is no choice of questions in the exam - all questions are compulsory. The exam in total lasts two hours and NEBOSH recommend that you spend:

- about half an hour on Section 1; and
- about one and a half hours on Section 2.

Exam Technique

In the exam, candidates can often struggle because they have not understood the question that is being asked. They can interpret questions wrongly and, as such, provide an answer for the question they think is in front of them but in reality is not. To try to overcome this issue, let's look at a step-by-step approach that you can adopt when answering exam questions:

Step 1. The first step is to read the question carefully. Be sure you know exactly what type of information the question is trying to elicit from you.

Step 2. Monitor the time. The 20-mark question in the first section should take around 25 minutes to answer, with five minutes' reviewing time. The eight-mark questions in Section 2 should take around eight minutes to answer. This will leave an accumulated time of ten minutes at the end of Section 2 to review your answers.

Step 3. Next, consider the marks available. For each mark to be awarded, the examiner will expect a piece of information to award the mark against.

Step 4. The next stage is to develop a plan – there are various ways to do this. Remind yourself again of the content of the question. Focus on key words that you have underlined on the examination paper to make sure you answer the question set. The answer plan is your aide-mémoire and can take the form of a list or a mind map that helps you unload information quickly and make sure you have enough factors (or things) in your answer that will attract the available marks. Keep re-reading the question to ensure your answer plan is going to answer the question set.

Step 5. When composing your answer, it is essential that you pay proper attention to the command word (e.g. outline, describe, identify, explain) that has been used in the question. Candidates lose marks if the wrong approach is taken. Remember you made a list to help your memory. NEBOSH will not be asking for a list anywhere on the paper, so if you replicate your answer plan in the answer, you will not gain the available marks. The command word informs you about the amount of information the examiner is expecting you to provide on the factors you have listed.

Command Words and Their Meaning

Command Word	Meaning
Describe	To give a detailed written account of the distinctive features of a subject. The account should be factual, without any attempt to explain.
Explain	To provide an understanding. To make an idea or relationship clear.
Give	To provide short, factual answers. NB: Normally a single word, phrase or sentence will be sufficient.
Identify	To give a reference to an item, which could be its name or title.
Outline	To indicate the principal features or different parts of.

When it comes to the exam, make sure you indicate clearly which is your Answer Plan and which is your Final Answer, so that the examiner can be sure to mark the correct one.

When writing your answer, you must ensure that the structure of the question appears in the structure of your answer. So, for example, if the question has a part (a) and a part (b), your answer must follow the same structure. Answer part (a) and label it clearly for the examiner as the answer to part (a). Then leave a gap (one line will do) and answer part (b) and label it clearly. The examiner must be able to see the two separate parts of your answer and it must be clear to them which parts are the answer to which. One long paragraph of text that contains all parts of the answer jumbled up together cannot win full marks, even if all of the relevant information is there.

Application of Command Words

Identify four kitchen appliances:

- *Toaster.*
- *Microwave.*
- *Washing Machine.*
- *Electric Kettle.*

Outline four kitchen appliances:

- *Toaster – cooks individual slices of bread.*
- *Microwave – heats food using short length radio waves.*
- *Washing Machine – cleans clothes by agitating them in water.*
- *Electric Kettle – uses a heating element to boil small quantities of water.*

Describe a washing machine:

A square metal box approximately 60cmx60cmx60cm with a door which opens in the front which is usually round and made of glass to view the washing. There is space within the machine to place approximately 7kg of laundry. Detergent and fabric softener are placed in a drawer and water is drawn via a pipe into the machine.

Explain how a washing machine cleans laundry:

The laundry is placed inside the machine drum by the operator. Detergent is placed within the drawer together with fabric softener. The correct operating temperature is selected on the control panel and the machine is started. Water is drawn into the drum together with the detergent and the drum moves to agitate the clothes and wash them. When this is complete, dirty water is drained away and the clothes rinsed with clean water before spinning at high speed to remove excess water.

You will find more guidance as you work through the course along with plenty of sample/practice questions. It's really important that you complete these and get in touch with your tutor if you have any queries or there is anything you are struggling with.

Taking into account what we have just covered on exam technique, look at the following question.

Exam Skills Practice

At the end of each element there is an Exam Skills question (or two) for you to attempt, with guidance on how to answer in addition to a suggested answer outline. This includes an Answer Plan – all of the points listed in this would attract marks and you will see most of them developed in the suggested answer itself.

Remember that when answering exam questions, information from additional reading and personal experience may be included. Examining bodies encourage this and it will enhance your answers.

There is a time estimate at the beginning of each Exam Skills activity. Don't worry if the activity takes you a little longer than this - the timings are just there as a rough guide.

Please feel free to contact your tutor if you have any queries or need any additional guidance.

QUESTION

Taking into account what we have just covered on exam technique, consider the following question.

Giving an example in **EACH** case, **outline** the purpose and legal status of existing:

(a) health and safety regulations; (4)

(b) HSE Approved Codes of Practice. (4)

Approaching the Question

Now think about the steps you would take to answer this question:

Step 1: The first step is to read the question carefully. Note that this question asks for an example in each case, so this would be worth one of the four marks on offer for each part. You are asked to provide an outline, so will need to structure your approach (a bullet-point list that will be developed into an outline).

Step 2: Next, consider the marks available. In this question, there are eight marks distributed evenly between two parts. Questions that are multi-part are often easier to answer because there are additional signposts in the question to keep you on track. In this question you have to give an example for each part and outline the purpose **and** legal status for each part. You will need to provide around eight or nine different pieces of information, including an example for each part of the question. The question should take around eight minutes in total.

Step 3: Now highlight the key words. In this case they might look like this:

Giving an example in **EACH** case, **outline** the purpose and legal status of existing:

(a) health and safety regulations; (4)

(b) HSE Approved Codes of Practice. (4)

Step 4: Read the question again to make sure you understand it and have a clear understanding of health and safety regulations and Approved Codes of Practice. (Re-read your notes if you need to.)

Step 5: The next stage is to develop a plan – there are various ways to do this. Remind yourself, first of all, that you need to be thinking about 'purpose, legal status and example' of legislation and an ACoP. When you see the action word 'outline', you need to give the most important features, but you must do more than provide a list. This question has two command words, because you need to 'give' an example - this means 'provide without an explanation'.

Your answer must be based on the key words you have highlighted. So, in this case we need to **give** examples in each case, **outline** the purpose and legal status of a piece of legislation and an ACoP.

Suggested Answer Outline

Plan

Regulations

- Can be introduced to implement European directives.
- Contain statutory duties.
- Prosecution or fines for breaches.
- Enforced by enforcement authority.
- Usually made by the Secretary of State with powers introduced under the Health and Safety at Work, etc. Act 1974.

ACoP

- Provide a recognised interpretation of legislation.
- Failure to comply may be cited in court in criminal proceedings.
- Must meet the ACoP standard or comply with an equal or better standard.
- Have semi-legal status.

Now have a go at the question yourself.

Example of How the Question Could be Answered

(a) *Regulations are usually introduced under the Health and Safety at Work, etc. Act 1974 by the Secretary of State, often to implement European directives. Regulations contain statutory duties which, if not met by the duty holder, may lead to prosecution and the imposition of fines. Regulations are enforced by enforcement officers working either for local government (councils) or the HSE who may issue enforcement notices if the requirements of the regulations are not being met. Examples of regulations are the Manual Handling Regulations 1992 or the Work at Height Regulations 2005.*

(b) *Approved Codes of Practice provide a recognised interpretation of regulations to enable the duty holder to comply with the required standard of duty. Failing to comply with an ACoP is in itself not an offence; however, the failure may be cited in court during criminal proceedings to demonstrate a breach of duty. The duty holder must then demonstrate that the standard they applied was equal to, or greater than, the standard required in the ACoP. An example is the Approved Code of Practice to the Control of Substances Hazardous to Health Regulations 2002.*

Reasons for Poor Marks Achieved by Candidates in Exam

- Not understanding the difference between regulations and an ACoP.
- Not following a structured approach, so not identifying the purpose and legal status and giving examples.
- Not answering the question at all. If you do not attempt all questions you cannot get any marks for the questions you omit.
- Citing incorrect examples:
  - The **HSWA** is not a set of regulations but an **Act** of Parliament (it's in the title!).
  - HSG65 (*Managing for Health and Safety*) is not an ACoP.

Element 2

Plan

Learning Outcomes

Once you've read this element, you'll understand how to:

1. Outline the key elements of a health and safety management system.
2. Explain the purpose and importance of setting policy for health and safety.
3. Describe the key features and appropriate content of an effective health and safety policy.

Contents

Health and Safety Management Systems

IN THIS SECTION...

- Two widely recognised Safety Management Systems (SMSs) exist for the systematic management of health and safety: HSG65 and OHSAS 18001.
- HSG65 is outlined in the HSE's guidance note 'Managing for Health and Safety' and can be summarised as Plan-Do-Check-Act (the PDCA cycle).
- OHSAS 18001 is an externally verified management standard that can be summarised as: Policy, Planning, Implementation and Operation; Checking and Corrective Action, Management Review, Continual Improvement.

Introduction

The management of workplace health and safety must be considered systematically within any organisation of significant size, in the same way as any other form of management. A systematic approach to management of an organisation's health and safety is referred to as a Safety Management System (SMS). There are two standard SMSs commonly used by organisations; HSG65 and OHSAS 18001. HSG65 is the HSE's own SMS published in a Guidance Note called "Managing for Health and Safety". OHSAS 18001 is the Occupational Health and Safety Management Systems standard published by the British Standards Institution (BSI). Organisations are free to develop their own SMS, but working to a recognised standard can be an advantage.

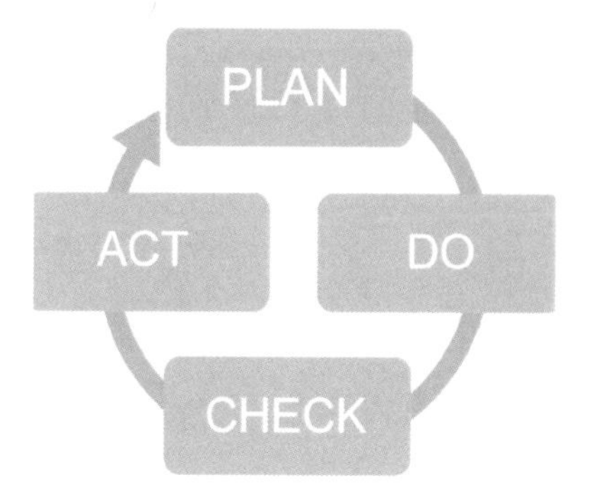

PDCA management cycle

Both SMSs are based on what is known as the 'PDCA management cycle'.

- **Plan.**
- **Do.**
- **Check.**
- **Act.**

We saw in Element 1 that the **Management of Health and Safety at Work Regulations** make it a legal requirement to have effective arrangements to *"plan, organise, control, monitor and review"* the preventive and protective measures – having a clearly defined SMS provides evidence that this is in place.

HSG65: Managing for Health and Safety

The key elements of the HSG65 SMS are shown graphically as:

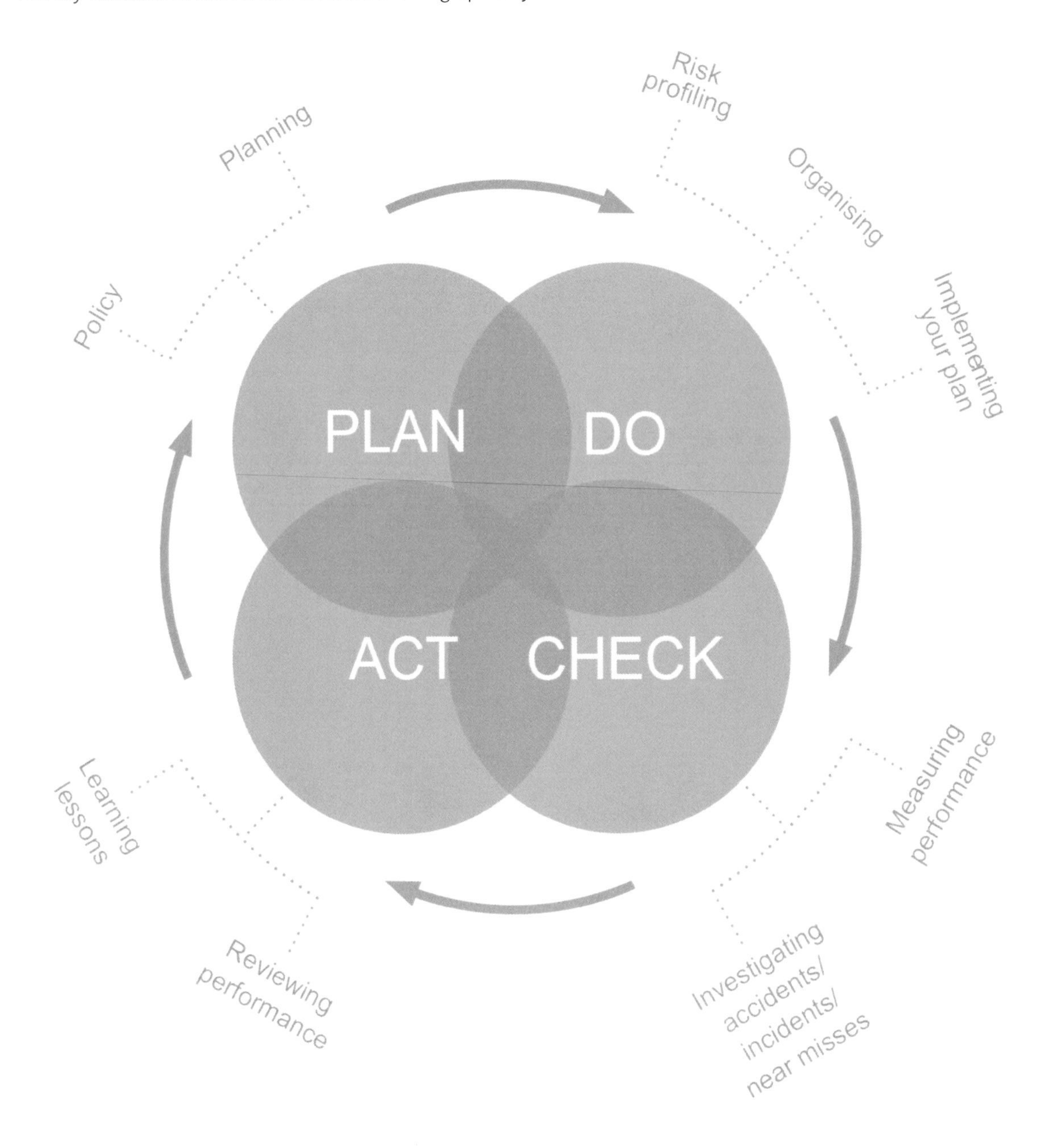

These can be explained simply as:

PLAN

Think about where you are now and where you need to be:

- Say what you want to achieve, who will be responsible for what, how you will achieve your aims, and how you will measure your success. This will form part of your **health and safety policy**, which you may need to write down, together with your plan to deliver it.

- Decide how you will measure performance. Think about ways to do this that go beyond looking at reactive indicators such as accident figures; look for active indicators such as the number of workplace inspections carried out or the results of housekeeping tours.
- Consider fire and other emergencies. Co-operate with anyone who shares your workplace and co-ordinate plans with them.
- Remember to **plan** for changes and identify any specific legal requirements that apply to you.

DO

- Identify your risk profile
  - Assess the risks, identify what could cause harm in the workplace, who it could harm and how, and what you will do to manage the risk.
  - Decide what the priorities are and identify the biggest risks.
- Organise your activities to deliver your plan

  In particular, aim to:
  - Involve workers and communicate, so that everyone is clear on what is needed and can discuss issues – develop positive attitudes and behaviours.
  - Provide adequate resources, including competent advice where needed.
- Implement your plan
  - Decide on the preventive and protective measures needed and put them in place.
  - Provide the right tools and equipment to do the job and keep them maintained.
  - Train and instruct, to ensure everyone is competent to carry out their work.
  - Supervise to make sure that arrangements are followed.

CHECK

- Measure your performance
  - Make sure that your plan has been implemented – 'paperwork' on its own is not a good performance measure.
  - Assess how well the risks are being controlled and if you are achieving your aims. In some circumstances, formal audits may be useful.
- Investigate the causes of accidents, incidents and near misses

ACT

- Review your performance
  - Learn from accidents and incidents, ill-health data, errors and relevant experience, including from other organisations.
  - Re-visit plans, policy documents and risk assessments to see if they need to be updated.
- Take action on lessons learnt, including from audit and inspection reports

  HSG65 is widely used by many organisations as the basis for their safety management system. The one significant drawback of HSG65 is that it is not a management standard that organisations can gain external certification/verification to. Organisations seeking external certification to a management standard have to use OHSAS 18001 instead.

OHSAS 18001: The Occupational Health and Safety Management System Standard

OHSAS 18001 is also based on the PDCA management cycle and is compatible with ISO 9001 (an internationally recognised quality management standard) and ISO 14001 (an internationally recognised environmental management standard). It provides a management standard that an organisation can be externally audited against. Successful certification to the management standard means that the organisation can demonstrate to other interested parties (such as clients and investors) that it has a robust safety management system that can stand up to close scrutiny.

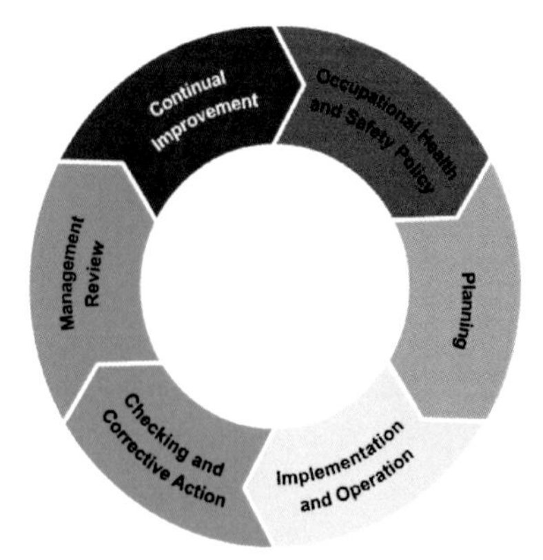

OHSAS 18001 safety management system

Occupational Health and Safety Policy (Plan)

This should state the overall health and safety objectives of the organisation and it should commit the organisation to compliance with legislation and continual improvement. It should be communicated to all employees and other interested parties and kept up to date by periodic review. It should be authorised by top management and, of course, be documented.

Planning (Plan)

Procedures have to be established, implemented and maintained for the effective:

- Identification of hazards and assessment and control of risks. This will include change management procedures. When controlling risk, a standard hierarchy of risk control will be used (see Element 3).
- Identification of any applicable law.
- Establishment of health and safety objectives and a management programme to achieve those objectives.

Implementation and Operation (Do)

- The necessary organisational structure and resources need to be put in place to implement the plans, though top management retain ultimate responsibility.
- People need to be competent to perform their designated roles and this may mean training and maintaining awareness.
- The organisation needs to have systems in place to ensure that health and safety information is communicated and that employees are consulted on health and safety matters.
- The management system must be documented and exercise control over those documents.
- Management arrangements for control of risks arising from operations must be documented.
- Plans and procedures must be made to cover potential emergencies.

Checking and Corrective Action (Check)

Procedures have to be established, implemented and maintained for the effective:

- Monitoring and measurement of health and safety performance (proactive, reactive, qualitative, quantitative).
- Evaluation of compliance to legal standards.
- Investigation of accidents/non-conformances to ensure that remedial actions are implemented.
- Recording of occupational health and safety monitoring data (including audit and review results).
- Internal auditing of the occupational health and safety management system.

Management Review (Act)

Top management must periodically review the health and safety management system to ensure it continues to be effective. This is all part of the drive for continual improvement of health and safety standards.

HINTS AND TIPS

You may need to go round the cycle more than once, particularly when:

- starting out;
- developing a new process, product, or service; or
- implementing any change.

MORE...

www.hse.gov.uk/managing/index.htm

www.hse.gov.uk/pubns/books/hsg65.htm

STUDY QUESTIONS

1. What are the elements of the PDCA Cycle outlined in 'Managing for Health and Safety' (HSG65)?
2. What are the elements of the safety management system outlined in 'OHSAS 18001: Occupational Health and Safety Management Systems'?

(Suggested Answers are at the end.)

The Purpose and Importance of a Health and Safety Policy

IN THIS SECTION...

- The health and safety policy of an organisation is an important document that sets out the organisation's aims with regards to health and safety, who is responsible for achieving these aims, and how the aims are to be achieved.
- The policy has a role in the decision-making of both senior management, who formulate it, and middle and junior management, who are required to implement it.
- Having a written health and safety policy is a legal requirement under **HSWA** Section 2(3) where an employer has five or more employees.

The Role of the Health and Safety Policy in Decision-Making

One foundation stone of good health and safety management in any organisation is the health and safety policy. A good health and safety policy sets out the organisation's general approach and commitment to achieving particular aims and objectives. It provides a framework of general and specific health and safety responsibilities for staff, and guidance on the detailed operational arrangements to be made to protect employees and others from harm as a result of workplace activities.

Health and safety policy

In particular, the policy should influence decision-making within the organisation. This will occur in two ways:

- In the first instance, senior management have to decide what kind of health and safety standards they are committing the organisation to and they will then have to allocate resources accordingly.
- In the second instance, other managers have to ensure that their decision-making is in line with the policy and does not work against the organisation's stated aims and objectives.

There is no one correct format or set of contents for a health and safety policy, but it must reflect the particular circumstances of the individual organisation: the hazards and risks, the size and the complexity of the organisation. The policy must therefore be developed and tailored to fit the particular organisation that it exists to serve. For example, the safety policy of a small, low-risk manufacturing company may be very different from that of a large, high-risk oil and gas multinational.

Legal Duties

The principal legal duty to prepare a health and safety policy is contained in Section 2(3) of **HSWA**:

- Section 2(3) requires an employer to prepare a written health and safety policy that will include a general statement of policy and the organisation and arrangements for carrying it out. This policy must be revised as necessary and brought to the attention of employees.

Subsequent legislation has made a written policy a legal requirement where the employer has five or more employees.

This legal duty to prepare a written policy is reinforced by **MHSWR**:

- Regulation 5 requires an employer to make arrangements for the effective planning, organisation, control, monitoring and review of the preventive and protective measures. These arrangements must be recorded where the employer has five or more employees.

MORE...

www.hse.gov.uk/business/policy.htm

STUDY QUESTIONS

3. In what circumstances may an employer be exempt from the requirement to provide a written statement of health and safety policy?
4. Under what legislative requirement do employers have a duty to prepare a health and safety policy?
5. Why might the health and safety policy of two organisations, both undertaking similar work, be different?

(Suggested Answers are at the end.)

The Key Features and Content of a Health and Safety Policy

IN THIS SECTION...

- A health and safety policy is usually presented in three parts: the General Statement of Intent, the Organisation section, and the Arrangements section.
- The General Statement of Intent outlines the importance that the organisation places on health and safety and the commitment that can be expected. It sets aims and objectives for the organisation to achieve. It is signed by the person in overall control of the organisation.
- The Organisation section highlights the roles and responsibilities that exist at all levels within the organisation. It shows the lines of responsibility and accountability.
- The Arrangements section provides the detail on how the organisation manages health and safety. It outlines the general arrangements that relate to health and safety management and the specific arrangements that relate to individual health and safety topics and issues.
- Health and safety policies have to be reviewed in order to stay current and relevant.

A policy is normally presented in three sections or elements:

- **General Statement of Intent** - the organisation's philosophy in relation to the management of health and safety.
- **Organisation** section - indicates the chain of command for health and safety management and identifies roles and responsibilities.
- **Arrangements** section - outlines the arrangements that exist for the effective management of health and safety in general terms (e.g. how risk assessments are to be carried out) and also deals with the management of specific issues (e.g. arrangements for ensuring the safety of visitors).

A policy is normally presented in three sections

General Statement of Intent

This spells out the organisation's overall approach to health and safety management, and its aims and objectives – and in this way can be seen as a vision for health and safety. It must commit the organisation to achieving legal compliance, and in many cases the commitment will be to achieving a higher standard than that set by the law, either as a matter of over-arching corporate policy or because of the nature of the organisation.

The Statement of Intent will usually recognise that managers and workers at all levels within the organisation have a part to play in implementing policy and will therefore state very clearly that every person must comply with the policy and that serious breaches of policy may be treated as disciplinary offences.

The General Statement of Intent should be:

- Signed by the person at the top of the organisation (Chief Executive Officer (CEO), Managing Director (MD), etc.) to authorise the policy and indicate that the policy commitment comes from the highest level.
- Dated to indicate when the current statement was prepared and provide a reference point for review.

TOPIC FOCUS

Aims

The Statement of Intent may recognise some general objectives that have to be achieved by the organisation, such as:

- Meeting legal obligations.
- Provision of a safe workplace, safe equipment and safe systems of work, information, instruction, training and supervision.
- Risk assessment of all relevant workplace activities.
- Performance monitoring.
- Provision of adequate resources, such as expert health and safety advice.
- Effective communication and consultation with workers.
- Send a Site Safety Report to the authority for approval.

Objectives (Targets)

The Statement of Intent may also set specific objectives or targets for the organisation to achieve. Targets are useful as they allow performance to be measured and provide a tangible goal for staff to aim for. They also help to drive continual improvement.

Possible targets might relate to:

- **Accident rates**: to achieve a reduction in the accident or ill-health rate.

  Targets may be set in relation to past performance or the performance of other similar organisations, or the industry as a whole. The process of comparing performance in this way is known as 'benchmarking'. So, if fatal accident rates in an industry as a whole are, for example, one for every 100,000 miles driven, the target for a particular organisation may be to achieve that standard or have a lower rate.

- **Active monitoring**: to complete successfully a number of active monitoring activities, e.g. successful completion of 90% of all supervisor safety inspections over a year.

Setting 'SMART' Objectives (Targets)

When health and safety objectives are set for an organisation, those objectives should be 'SMART'.

The acronym 'SMART' refers to the idea that objectives should be:

- **Specific** – a clearly defined, precise objective.
- **Measurable** – it is possible to measure achievement of (or towards) the target; usually by quantifying the objective.
- **Achievable** – it can be done.
- **Reasonable** – within the timescale set and with the resources allocated.
- **Time-bound** – a deadline or timescale is set for completion of the objective.

So, for example, the objective: "improve the safety culture of the organisation" is not smart because it fails to meet many of the criteria of a smart objective. It is not specific, in that it does not identify a precise target to be achieved; it is not easily measurable (as will be discussed in Element 3) and it does not have a deadline when success should have been achieved.

However, the objective "Review all 48 risk assessments within a 12-month period" is a smart objective. The target is precisely defined, a number is given that allows easy measurement of success and a timescale has been allocated.

When setting health and safety objectives, consideration should be given to:

- Who is going to set objectives – the involvement of senior management, perhaps with guidance from health and safety practitioners/advisers.
- How objectives will be set at each functional level – objectives need to be set at different levels or within different parts of the organisation to achieve organisational goals. This can be achieved by setting and agreeing personal targets with individuals through the job appraisal and review process.
- Legal and other requirements – objectives must recognise legal standards and other requirements set by, for example, corporate policy, insurance companies, etc.
- Hazards and risks – the hazards inherent in the workplace and the risks created must be taken into account when setting objectives. If this is not done, then the organisation may pursue objectives that are irrelevant or that address only trivial matters.
- Technological options – as technology changes, organisations should take advantage of that new technology and set objectives accordingly.
- Financial, operational, and business requirements – health and safety objectives should integrate with financial, operational and business objectives so that there is no conflict of goals.
- Views of interested parties – for objectives to be achievable, it is important that some element of consultation occurs and that the views of interested parties are considered. Employees (through their representatives), supervisors, managers, contractors, clients, customers, landlords, co-occupiers, suppliers, manufacturers and designers may all be able to contribute to the health and safety objectives of an organisation.

Organisation

This section of the health and safety policy deals with people and their operational duties in relation to health and safety. It outlines the chain of command for health and safety management and identifies the roles and responsibilities of staff. It is standard practice for this section to include an organisation chart showing the lines of responsibility and accountability (in terms of health and safety management). This chart also shows the lines of communication and the feedback routes that exist within the organisation.

The following figure shows a typical organisation chart for a company. The grey lines show "line management responsibility" flowing down through the structure. The green lines show the "functional responsibility" that the health and safety manager has for providing advice at all levels of the organisation.

The orange lines show the lines of communication and feedback up through the structure.

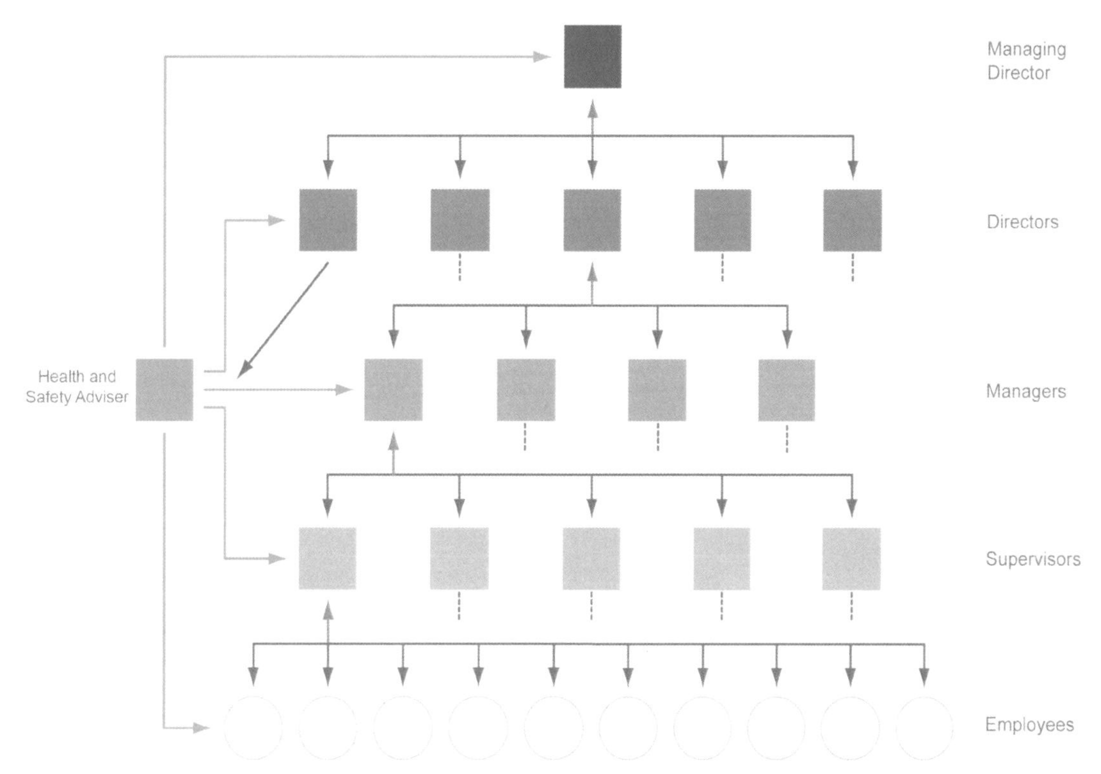

Health and Safety Organisation Chart

The Organisation section will usually reflect the management hierarchy within the organisation and allocate responsibilities accordingly:

Staff from all levels of an organisation

- **The CEO or MD** – is ultimately responsible and accountable for the entire organisation.
- **Management at all levels** – is responsible for ensuring that all appropriate safety measures are in place and being carried out effectively within their sphere of management control. This might be done by breaking the management hierarchy down into discrete layers and allocating responsibilities to each layer, e.g. senior managers' responsibilities, middle managers' responsibilities, supervisors' responsibilities.
- **All employees** – are responsible for acting safely at all times in the course of their duties at work.

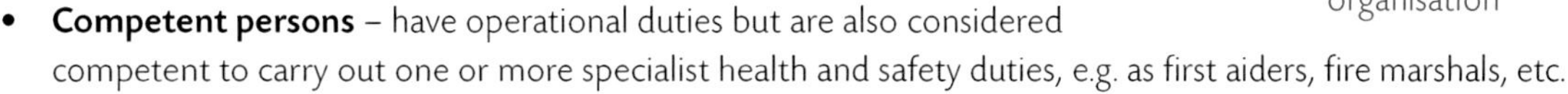

- **Competent persons** – have operational duties but are also considered competent to carry out one or more specialist health and safety duties, e.g. as first aiders, fire marshals, etc.

- **Specialist health and safety practitioners** – are responsible for providing advice to support management and employees in achieving safety.

Arrangements

The Arrangements section is often the largest section of the policy. "Arrangements" really means "procedures", so this section deals with the general arrangements that exist to manage health and safety and the specific arrangements that are necessary to deal with particular risks relevant to the organisation and its activities.

TOPIC FOCUS

General health and safety management arrangements:

- Carrying out risk assessments.
- Identifying and supplying health and safety information, instruction and training.
- Accident and near-miss reporting, recording and investigation.
- Consultation with workers on health and safety matters.
- Developing safe systems of work and permit-to-work systems to control hazards.
- Details of specific hazards to the organisation, e.g. hazardous substances or lone working.
- Welfare and first-aid provision.
- Housekeeping.
- Fire safety and prevention.
- Emergency procedures.
- Communication of health and safety matters, including hazards and control measures.
- Compliance monitoring, including auditing of systems but also measuring workplace parameters, e.g. noise, to assess the effectiveness of the arrangements.

All of the general health and safety management issues will be relevant to all workplaces; they are generic issues. However, the practical arrangements made for the management of these issues will have to be tailored to suit the organisation.

Depending on the workplace, **specific** health and safety arrangements will also have to be developed to deal with particular risks.

The list of possible arrangements that might be required can be long and is dependent on the problems and issues faced by the organisation in question. For example, a lorry haulage company will have a set of arrangements to manage transport risk, but an office-based company will not.

Examples of specific risks and problems within an organisation that may need detailed arrangements include:

- Lone working.
- Noise-exposure control.
- Vibration-exposure control.
- Control of exposure to toxic materials.
- Crowd control arrangements.
- Control of transport risks.
- Specific health surveillance requirements.
- Waste disposal.

Not all organisations will have all of these risks – these are 'specific' to the organisation and its functions.

Reviewing Policy

A health and safety policy should not be considered as rigid and unchanging. Instead, it should be subject to regular review so that it remains current and relevant. In this way it can be considered a 'live' document.

It is good practice to review policy on a regular basis, e.g. annually. However, there are other circumstances which could give rise to reviews, which can be thought of as technological, organisational or legal.

TOPIC FOCUS

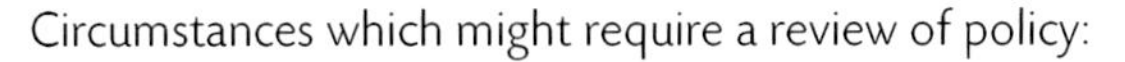

Circumstances which might require a review of policy:

- Changes to key personnel, e.g. a new CEO or MD.
- Changes to the management structure of the organisation.
- A management take-over.
- Changes to the type of work that the organisation does.
- Recommendation in a safety audit.
- Request from a third party, such as an insurance company or client.

The aim of the review is to make sure that the policy is up to date and accurate. The date of the previous review should be recorded on policy documents to indicate how current they are.

MORE...

www.hse.gov.uk/business/policy.htm

STUDY QUESTIONS

6. What are the three key elements of a health and safety policy? What does each section contain?
7. Who should sign the policy statement?
8. What health and safety responsibilities do all workers have?
9. What does a safety organisation chart show?
10. What circumstances might require a review of policy?

(Suggested Answers are at the end.)

Summary

This element has dealt with health and safety policies.

In particular, this element has:

- Outlined the HSG65 SMS: Plan-Do-Check-Act.
- Outlined the OHSAS 18001 SMS: Policy, Planning, Implementation and Operation, Checking and Corrective Action, Management Review, Continual Improvement.
- Identified the health and safety policy of an organisation as an important document that sets out what the organisation's aims are with regard to health and safety, who is responsible for achieving those aims, and how the aims are to be achieved.
- Identified the legal requirement, under Section 2(3) of **HSWA**, for the employer to prepare a written policy where he has five or more employees, bring it to his employees' attention and keep it under review.
- Explained that the policy is usually presented in three parts: the General Statement of Intent, the Organisation section and the Arrangements section:
  - The General Statement of Intent communicates the importance that the organisation places on health and safety, the commitment that can be expected and the aims and objectives for the organisation to achieve. It is signed by the person in overall control of the organisation.
  - The Organisation section deals with the roles and responsibilities that exist at all levels within the organisation and indicates the lines of responsibility and accountability.
  - The Arrangements section provides the detail on how the organisation manages health and safety. It outlines the general arrangements that relate to health and safety management and the specific arrangements that relate to individual health and safety topics and issues.
- Noted that health and safety policies have to be reviewed in order to stay current and relevant and that reviews might be carried out periodically or in response to changes, such as those to key personnel or management structure, changes in technology or legal changes.

Exam Skills

QUESTION

(a) **Identify** the legal requirements whereby employers must prepare a written statement of their health and safety policy. (2)

(b) **Outline** reasons why organisations should set health and safety targets. (6)

Approaching the Question

Think now about the steps you would take to answer the question:

1. The first step is to read the question carefully. Note that this question asks you to identify the legal requirements to prepare a written safety policy and to outline reasons for having safety targets. To identify something, you need to select and name the legislation and requirements. For an outline, you need to give the most important reasons why organisations should set safety targets.

2. Next, consider the marks available. In this question, there are eight marks, so it is expected that around eight or nine different pieces of information should be provided. Questions that are split into parts (this one is split into two parts worth two and six marks respectively) are often easier to pick up marks on, because the signposts NEBOSH use are so much easier to see. In the first part, the question asks you to 'identify' and is worth two marks, so citing the legislation will get one of those marks. The second part is an outline of why organisations should set health and safety targets and is worth six marks, so you will need six points in this section. The question should take around eight minutes in total.

3. Now highlight the key words. In this case, they might look like this:

   (a) **Identify** the legal requirements whereby employers must prepare a written statement of their health and safety policy. (2)

   (b) **Outline** reasons why organisations should set health and safety targets. (6)

4. Read the question again to make sure you understand it and have a clear understanding of health and safety policy and safety targets. (Re-read your notes if you need to.)

5. The next stage is to develop a plan – there are various ways to do this. Remind yourself, first of all, that you need to be thinking about 'legal requirements for a written health and safety policy' for the first part; and 'reasons why health and safety targets should be set' for the second part. The action word 'Identify' tells you to select and name the relevant requirements. When you see the action word 'Outline', you need to give the most important features. So, the answer plan will take the form of a bullet-pointed list that you need to develop into a full answer.

Your answer must be based on the key words you have highlighted. So, in this case we need to identify legal requirements for preparing a written health and safety policy and outline reasons why we have targets.

Suggested Answer

Plan

Legal Requirements
• HSW Act 1974, Section 2(3). • Must be written if five or more employees. • Bring to the attention of employees.
Why Safety Targets?
• Management commitment. • Focus on important issues. • Motivate staff. • Encourage ownership. • Enable performance measurement. • Identify improvements made. • Identify trends. • Enable review of performance.

Now have a go at the question yourself.

Example of How the Question Could be Answered

(a) *An employer has a duty to prepare a written statement of their health and safety policy as a requirement of the Health and Safety at Work, etc. Act 1974, when they employ five or more persons. Having prepared a written statement the employer also has a duty to bring the policy to the attention of their employees.*

(b) *By setting targets for health and safety an organisation's management are making a clear statement of their commitment to monitoring and meeting the standards set for health and safety. Targets enable management to prioritise and focus resources on issues where target levels are not being met. Employees are likely to be motivated to achieve a target set, e.g. number of hours without an accident exceeding the previous month's total. Targets are also likely to encourage ownership in health and safety - employees being involved in the attainment of a target are likely to strive to meet that target, which is likely to encourage safe behaviour. Management may well want to measure tangible gains in health and safety to justify expenditure and effort in supporting improvement programmes. Implicit in setting of targets is the measurement of the activity being targeted - management may be able to identify trends from this activity to anticipate whether targets will be met, exceeded or failed. Targets enable management to meet the standards set by the safety management system used, e.g. zero tolerance to not wearing PPE.*

Reasons for Poor Marks Achieved by Candidates in Exam

- Citing the wrong regulations, e.g. quoting the **Management of Health and Safety at Work Regulations** to find the requirements for a health and safety policy.
- Providing poor answers to part (b), possibly because of time constraints having overrun on previous questions.
- Not outlining a wide enough spectrum of reasons to set targets (six marks were available) and going into great detail on focusing on improvement which ultimately can only be worth one or two marks.

Element 3

Do

Learning Outcomes

Once you've read this element, you'll understand how to:

1. Outline the organisational health and safety roles and responsibilities of employers, directors, managers and supervisors.
2. Explain the concept of health and safety culture and its significance in the management of health and safety in an organisation.
3. Outline the human factors which influence behaviour at work in a way that can affect health and safety.
4. Explain how health and safety behaviour at work can be improved.
5. Explain the principles and practice of risk assessment.
6. Explain the general principles of prevention.
7. Identify the key sources of health and safety information.
8. Explain what factors should be considered when developing and implementing a safe system of work for general activities.
9. Explain the role and function of a permit-to-work system.
10. Outline the need for emergency procedures and the arrangements for contacting emergency services.
11. Outline the requirements for, and effective provision of, first aid in the workplace.

Contents

Organisational Roles of Directors, Managers and Supervisors

IN THIS SECTION...

- **Directors, managers** and **supervisors** have a duty to ensure that their organisation meets its legal obligations. In particular, they are responsible for planning, delivering, monitoring and reviewing policy.
- Senior managers must demonstrate clear commitment to health and safety by allocating adequate resources, defining roles and responsibilities, appointing a 'champion' at board level, appointing competent advisers and reviewing performance at a board level.

Directors and **senior managers** give an organisation its direction and set its priorities. They decide what the organisation does and how it does it. In effect, they control the corporate body. They are, therefore, responsible for ensuring that all of the legal requirements that rest with the employer are met. And, as we've seen in Element 1, Section 37 of **HSWA** makes it clear that directors and senior managers can be prosecuted for offences committed by the corporate body if they consented or connived in the offence or were negligent in their duties.

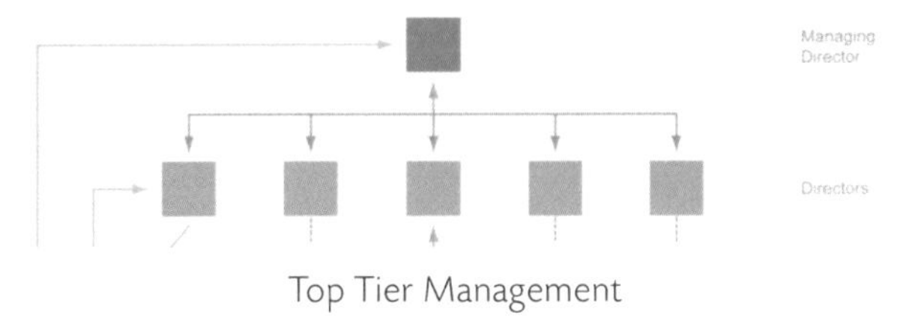

Top Tier Management

The HSE publication "Leading Health and Safety at Work" (INDG417) provides guidance to directors and senior managers in organisations of all sizes. It highlights four key areas for action:

- **Plan** - by establishing a health and safety policy that is an integral part of the organisation's culture, with board members taking an active lead in promoting health and safety throughout the organisation.
- **Deliver** - the policy through an effective management system that ensures that risks are dealt with sensibly, responsibly and proportionately (this clearly links to HSG65 and other SMSs).
- **Monitor** - to provide the board with reports on the performance of their policy.
- **Review** - performance to allow the board to establish whether the management system is effective in managing risks and protecting people.

Middle managers and **supervisors** are involved in the day-to-day operational running of the organisation so are responsible for the health and safety standards within the operations under their control. Their operational areas of responsibility are normally defined in the Organisation section of the policy and illustrated by the organisation chart.

Middle Management

Managers and supervisors will be operationally responsible for the health and safety of:

- The staff that work directly for them (their direct reports).
- Staff lower down in the organisational chart (below their direct reports).
- The areas and activities under their control.

Demonstrating Top Management Commitment

Directors and senior managers are not always closely involved in the day-to-day management of the operational side of an organisation. Their role does not always involve 'doing' (except in smaller organisations), but it does involve setting strategy.

Directors and senior managers can demonstrate their commitment to health and safety through their strategic thinking by:

- Ensuring availability of resources so the occupational health and safety management system is established, implemented and maintained.
- Defining roles and responsibilities so that the line management responsibility and accountability for health and safety is clear.
- Appointing a member of top management with specific responsibility for health and safety so that it is 'championed' at board level.
- Appointing one or more competent persons (including specialists where applicable) and adequate resources to provide assistance in meeting the organisation's health and safety obligations.
- Being involved in the engagement and management of contractors, demonstrating the organisation's health and safety responsibility to third parties.
- Taking an active role in the review of the organisation's health and safety performance through participation in management reviews. Board level reviews may also be carried out annually.

Directors and senior managers have an enormous influence over their organisation and its priorities. This influence does not simply come from their strategic decision-making, but also from the way they are perceived by those lower in the management hierarchy. They must demonstrate clear commitment and leadership with regard to health and safety.

MORE...

www.hse.gov.uk/leadership/index.htm

The influence of visible management commitment and leadership on safety culture is discussed later in this element.

STUDY QUESTION

1. Outline the four key action areas highlighted in the HSE publication *Leading Health and Safety at Work* (INDG417).

(Suggested Answer is at the end.)

The Concept and Significance of Safety Culture

IN THIS SECTION...

- The safety culture of an organisation is the way that all the people within the organisation think and feel about health and safety and how this translates into behaviour. It can be defined as the shared attitudes, values, beliefs and behaviours relating to health and safety.
- There is a strong link between safety culture and health and safety performance. Organisations with a strong, positive culture tend to have good performance, whereas those with a weak, negative culture perform poorly.
- The safety culture of an organisation can be assessed by looking at indicators such as accidents, sickness rates, absenteeism, staff turnover, compliance with rules and worker complaints.
- Workers are often influenced by their peers - the people around them at work who do not have any direct authority over them. This 'peer group pressure' occurs indirectly by social interaction and can have a significant effect on behaviour. The influence of peer group pressure is a good indicator of safety culture.

Definition

All organisations have a 'culture'. It is not written down, or even easily stated. It is a subtle mix of formal and informal rules, relationships, values, customs, etc., which, taken together, describe the distinctive 'feel' of the organisation. On one level, this is to do with how the organisation gets things done – its particular way of working. On another level, it is to do with how people perceive the organisation, e.g. how friendly it is.

Organisational culture is a characteristic of the organisation that exists at every level, from senior management to 'shop-floor' workers. No one person determines the culture of the organisation; all staff working for the organisation determine it collectively.

Organisations can be described as having a 'health and safety culture' (or safety culture) in much the same way.

The safety culture of an organisation is the way that everyone within the organisation thinks and feels about health and safety and how this translates into their behaviour.

All organisations have a 'culture'

DEFINITION 

SAFETY CULTURE

The shared attitudes, values, beliefs and behaviours relating to health and safety.

The Correlation between Culture and Performance

An organisation will have either a positive safety culture or a negative one.

Positive Culture

In an organisation with a positive safety culture, the majority of the workers think and feel that health and safety is important. There is a strong policy and clear leadership from the top because senior management have this attitude, which runs through the whole organisation, from top to bottom. Managers think about the health and safety implications of their decisions and workers share the same view and work safely.

Everyone works safely because they want to. That is the way that things are done in their organisation and that is how everybody else is behaving too.

People in the organisation who do not share this view are in the minority and are likely to come round to the group way of thinking and acting. This is because the culture of an organisation tends to be absorbed by its workers over time. Workers who do not adjust to the group way of thinking may either leave, because they don't feel that they fit in, or possibly be dismissed for working unsafely.

A company with a positive safety culture - all members of staff appreciate the importance of safety

In an organisation like this you can see that there is a clear link between safety culture and health and safety performance. People work safely, so there will be fewer accidents and less ill health. It is also easy to see why organisations strive to create a strong, positive safety culture because when there is one, it has a direct influence on worker behaviour.

Negative Culture

In an organisation with a weak, negative safety culture, the majority of workers think and feel that health and safety is not important; they are poorly educated in health and safety and see it as unnecessary or not important. There is a lack of clear direction and leadership from senior management. Managers do not think about health and safety in their decision-making and so let other priorities, such as productivity, dictate their actions. Workers behave unsafely, often because they do not know any better.

A workplace with a negative safety culture, resulting in unsafe behaviour

Safety-conscious workers are in the minority and are likely to come round to the group way of thinking and acting over time; if not, they may well leave because they do not like the organisational culture and feel unsafe in the work situation.

You can see that in an organisation like this there will be a lack of attention to health and safety, standards will be low, behaviour will be poor and accidents may occur as a result.

Indicators Used to Assess Culture

It makes sense to try to assess an organisation's safety culture to see whether it is strong and positive, or if there is room for improvement. But the safety culture of an organisation is quite difficult to assess directly because there is no one single feature or item that can be measured. Safety culture is partly defined as how people think and feel, their attitudes, their beliefs and their priorities. These are intangible concepts and almost impossible to measure. So, rather than trying to assess the safety culture directly, it is perhaps better to assess it indirectly by looking at the tangible outputs that can be used as indicators. There is no single indicator that can be used to assess safety culture; instead several indicators must be examined together.

Accidents

Accident records can be used to work out how many accidents are happening as a rate, (e.g. number of accidents per 100,000 hours worked - more on this in Element 4). The accident rate for a particular organisation can be compared with the:

- Organisation's performance in previous years. This will indicate whether the accident rate is increasing or decreasing. A decreasing rate might be seen as an indicator of a positive safety culture.

- Rate for other organisations that do the same work, or the industry average (often published by the authorities). This is the process of **benchmarking, which we covered in Element 2.** An accident rate that is higher than national average might be seen as an indicator of a negative safety culture.

Looking at the standard of investigation that follows an accident and the effort that is put into preventing a recurrence is another way of using accidents as an indicator of safety culture. In an organisation:

- With a **positive** safety culture, much time and effort will go into investigating accidents, writing investigation reports and introducing follow-up action to prevent a recurrence.
- With a **negative** safety culture, superficial accident investigations are carried out, reports are of poor quality and follow-up action is either not taken, or is ineffective and may focus on blaming the worker rather than identifying why it happened.

Sickness Rates

A lot of ill health is caused, or made worse, by work. For example, in many countries, a huge number of working days are lost due to back pain and a significant proportion of that back pain will have been caused or made worse by the work that individuals are doing. So sickness rates can be used in the same way that accident rates are, as an indicator of safety culture.

Absenteeism

A high level of worker absenteeism indicates that workers are either not able, or not willing, to come to work. If they are not able, this might indicate that they are suffering ill health caused or worsened by work, as we noted above. If they are not willing, it indicates that they are withholding their labour for some reason. This is usually caused by poor workforce morale, which in turn can sometimes be linked to poor safety culture.

Staff Turnover

An organisation with a positive safety culture is often a good place to work. Workers feel safe, morale is good, training is available, and workers are consulted about their working conditions. As a result, workers stay with their employer for a long period of time, so low staff turnover may indicate a good safety culture, while high staff turnover may indicate the opposite.

Compliance with Safety Rules

In an organisation with a positive safety culture, the majority of workers want to work safely, so they comply with the safety rules and procedures laid down by the organisation. When a formal, or informal, safety inspection or audit is carried out, a high level of compliance is seen. The safety culture has influenced workers' behaviour in a positive way.

Where there is a negative safety culture, quite the reverse is apparent. Workers do not follow the rules, either because they do not know what they are doing (perhaps due to poor training) or because they know the rules but do not want to follow them (perhaps due to poor attitude). Workers are free to break the rules because of poor supervision; they know that they will not be punished.

Complaints About Working Conditions

There is an obvious link between safety culture and the number and type of complaints made by workers (and workers' safety representatives) to management. An organisation with a positive culture may actively encourage complaints, but few serious ones will be made. An organisation with a negative safety culture may actively discourage workers from complaining and many of the complaints made will be legitimate and serious ones.

Influence of Peers

When people are put together into groups they interact. Some individuals will come to have a lot of influence over the group; others will have little influence. In this way, a 'hierarchy' (often known as a "pecking order") is established within the group. Certain ways of behaving will become the 'norm', which will often be established by the more influential members of the group. A person wishing to become a member of the group will have to comply with the group norms. This pressure to comply with group norms is 'peer group pressure'.

Peer group pressure can influence the thinking about safety-related behaviour

Peer group pressure is an important factor to take into account when thinking about safety-related behaviour. If a group is already working safely then peer group pressure will keep most people in that group in line. But if the group is working unsafely then peer group pressure will tend to force more and more workers to behave unsafely in an attempt to fit in. Even though workers may know that what they are doing is wrong and may want to do it the right way, the pressure to comply with the group overcomes their personal apprehensions.

The behaviour of peer groups and the influence that peer group pressure has been allowed to exert on worker behaviour is often a good indicator of safety culture. In an organisation with a positive culture, peer group pressure is in line with safe behaviour. In an organisation with a negative culture, peer group pressure is driving unsafe behaviours and this has not been challenged by management.

MORE... www.

www.hse.gov.uk/humanfactors/topics/culture.htm

STUDY QUESTIONS

2. Define 'health and safety culture'.
3. How do an individual's peers exert influence over his/her behaviour?

(Suggested Answers are at the end.)

Human Factors Influencing Safety-Related Behaviour

IN THIS SECTION...

- Of critical importance to health and safety management is individual worker behaviour. One worker may behave in an ideal manner, but another may not and this unsafe behaviour may endanger themselves and others.
- Three significant factors influence a worker's behaviour:
  - The organisation – characteristics of the organisation that they are working for.
  - The job – the task that they are carrying out.
  - The individual – their personal characteristics.
- Key characteristics of an individual worker that influence their safety-related behaviour include their attitude (how they think about a particular safety issue) and their ability to perceive the hazards and risks present in their workplace.

Introduction

One issue of critical importance to health and safety management is the way that individual workers behave. It is estimated that well over half of all workplace accidents are caused by unsafe acts: the poor safety-related behaviour of a worker. It is not enough to dismiss this as being due to carelessness; this simply blames the worker and is ineffective at identifying underlying causes or corrective actions. Instead, we must look at how "human factors" influence working practices; we have to understand why people behave the way they do at work.

Factors which influence behaviour

If we can understand that, then it may be possible to:

- Correct poor behaviour when it is identified by removing the cause of that behaviour.
- Anticipate poor behaviour before it occurs and introduce changes to reduce the likelihood of it occurring.

Individual, Job and Organisational Factors

Why is it that one worker behaves safely at work, but another does not, even though working conditions for both workers are the same?

Why is it that a worker may behave safely doing one job, but then unsafe practices start to creep into their behaviour when they are switched to another job?

Why is it that a worker behaves poorly when working for one organisation, but then leaves and starts to work for another company and behaves in an entirely different manner?

The answer to these three questions is 'human factors'. This phrase refers to a range of issues that influence a person's safety-related behaviour when they are at work.

These issues can be grouped under three main headings:

- **Individual factors** – characteristics of the individual.
- **Job factors** – characteristics of the job or task that they are performing.
- **Organisational factors** – characteristics of the organisation that they are working for.

Organisational Factors

These are the characteristics of the organisation that influence workers' behaviour.

Organisational factors include:

- **Safety culture** of the organisation – the way that this culture is gradually absorbed by the individual (as already discussed).
- **Commitment and leadership** from management – whether this is visibly demonstrated outside of the boardroom (since behaviour in the boardroom is not witnessed by most of the workers in an organisation).
- **Resources** – whether financial or provision of adequate time and personnel to carry out tasks safely organisations must adequately resource safety.
- **Work patterns** – such as shift systems, work at night or extended hours that can lead to adverse effects on health and fatigue, that in turn can lead to poor performance on tasks which require attention and increase the risks associated with safety-critical work.
- **Communications** – how effective the organisation is at using various communication methods to convey health and safety messages and information out to the workforce and how well the organisation then checks understanding of those messages. Provision of effective methods of communication can encourage workers to behave safely as they will understand the requirements and understand why safety remains important to the organisation.
- **Levels of supervision** – the presence or absence of, and the competence of, supervision (in the context of health and safety) and the way that poor safety-related behaviour is dealt with. For example, in an organisation that undertakes engineering maintenance work, the presence of competent supervisors to oversee that work is critical as a check to prevent both rule-breaking behaviour and human error.
- **Consultation** and worker involvement – the extent to which workers are involved in the management of health and safety issues and in the decision-making. process.
- **Training** – how good the organisation is at identifying health and safety training needs and opportunities and how well it then meets those needs to create well-informed, competent staff.

Consultation with workers

Job Factors

These are the various characteristics of a worker's job that influence their safety-related behaviour and may involve:

- **Task** – the characteristics of the work itself, in particular the ergonomic requirements (we will consider ergonomics later). For example, the need to bend or stoop over when carrying out a task requires the task to be adapted to best suit the worker concerned. In the absence of ergonomic design, workers will find the most comfortable way of working and this may not be the safest way.

DEFINITION 

ERGONOMICS

The adjustment of the workplace to suit the needs of the individual worker to avoid injuries such as back pain.

- **Workload** – the amount of work, rate of work, deadlines and variety of work that individuals have to cope with and the degree to which these are under the direct control of the worker or imposed externally.
- **Environment** – the workplace conditions such as space, lighting, noise, temperature and humidity and the way that these parameters are controlled so as to minimise their impact on worker performance. For example, workers in a steel foundry may have to undertake physical labour in a high temperature environment where there is the potential for dehydration, heat stress and heat stroke. Workers may find ways of working, that are not necessarily safe, in order to minimise physical exertion. They may also start to suffer degradation in physical and mental performance as a result of heat stress.
- **Displays and controls** – the design of these and the way that poorly designed displays and controls can contribute to the likelihood of human error. For example, displays that are difficult to view and critical displays that are out of the operator's normal field of view.
- **Procedures** – the existence of, and quality of, working procedures. A lack of written procedures or poorly written procedures that are out of date, overly complex or impractical can be a reason for employees not to comply. To be effective, procedures should be accurate, concise, use familiar language and they must be do-able.

Individual Factors

People bring to their job their own personal mix of knowledge and experience, skills, attitudes, and personality. These individual characteristics influence behaviour in complex and significant ways. Some of these characteristics cannot be changed, but others can.

Competence

A combination of knowledge, experience, training and ability, that brings a person to a level where they are able to perform to an acceptable standard and where they are aware of their own limitations.

Skills

Each individual has skills that they have developed over time; whether these are technical engineering skills or those of a great communicator, they can all be very useful in the improvement of safety within the organisation. Equally, fitting a person with the wrong skill set into the wrong role is unwise - a very shy person will not be happy making a company safety presentation to the workforce.

Personality

We can influence someone's attitude to health and safety, we can increase their skills and develop their competence but their personality remains largely fixed – it's who we are.

Attitude

A person's point of view or way of looking at something; how they think and feel about it.

In the context of workplace behaviour, attitudes are important because a worker's attitude will make them more or less likely to behave safely. For example, if a worker's attitude to a machine guard is that the guard is great, because it is there to stop their arm being cut off, then that worker is very unlikely to remove the guard in any circumstances. But if the worker's attitude is that the guard is unnecessary, over-the-top, put there to tick a box or to make the job harder, then that worker is likely to remove the machine guard at the earliest opportunity.

Changing attitudes is notoriously difficult but can be done using various methods, such as education and training, high impact interventions, enforcement and consultation, and involvement in the decision-making process.

Motivation

The thing that is making a person do what they do. In the context of health and safety, it is important to understand a worker's motivation for carrying out their work in a safe or unsafe way because that motivation can then be changed. Workers often behave unsafely not simply because they are wilful, but because they perceive a reward and they think that the risk is worth the reward. Their unsafe behaviour is incentivised. For example, a worker who can make more money by taking an unsafe shortcut is far more likely to take that shortcut if they think they can get away with it.

Risk Perception

Risk perception can be defined as the way that a person interprets information detected by their senses.

Some hazards in the workplace cannot be detected by human senses, (e.g. carbon monoxide gas is colourless, odourless and tasteless yet deadly at relatively low concentrations) so the risk associated with these hazards will not be perceived.

People with some form of sensory impairment may not be able to correctly detect hazards in a workplace. For example, a partially sighted person may not be able to see trip hazards on the floor so they are at greater risk from these hazards than their sighted colleagues.

A colour-blind worker may not be able to differentiate correctly between red and green and this may create risk to themselves and others. That is why some jobs require an eye test and colour blindness would prevent recruitment, (e.g. airline pilots). Both of these examples deal with a defective sense (eyesight). Any form of sensory impairment, whether it is sight, hearing, smell, touch or even taste, may mean that a person is unable to correctly perceive the world around them. This might have health and safety implications.

A sensory impairment can be created in the workplace if, for example, conditions prevent the information reaching the senses. PPE is designed to protect, but in many cases it can cause an impairment (gloves can result in a loss of touch and dexterity, hearing protection prevents warnings being detected, etc.). In addition, background noise, or high levels of odour can also mask issues that we would usually be able to detect.

However, perception goes beyond this simple 'sensory impairment' issue to also cover the way that a person's brain interprets the information sent to it by the senses. A person with fully functioning senses can still make errors in the way that they interpret sensory information.

Optical illusions work using this principle. Which centre dot is larger?

They are, in fact, the same size. Your eyes work, but the brain interprets the information incorrectly.

Factors that can distort a person's perception of hazard and risk include:

- Illness.
- Stress.
- Fatigue.
- Drugs and alcohol.
- Previous experiences.
- Training and education.
- Use of PPE.
- Workplace conditions such as high levels of noise.

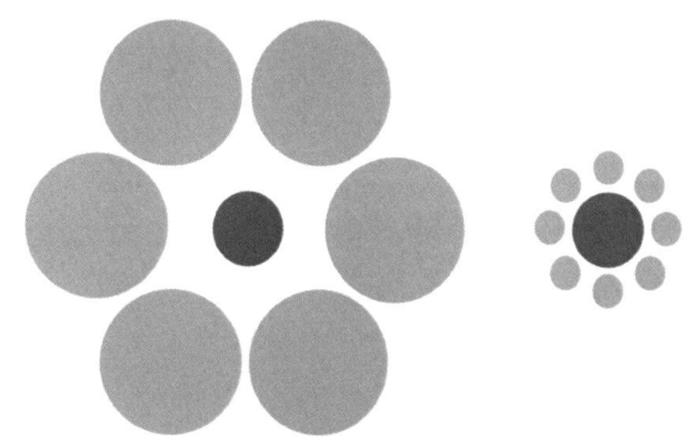

Optical illusion

MORE...

www.

www.hse.gov.uk/humanfactors/index.htm

Reducing error and influencing behaviour (HSG48) available from the HSE website.

STUDY QUESTIONS

4. Identify the three factors that impact on a person's health-and-safety-related behaviour.
5. Outline the key job factors that can impact on safety-related behaviour.
6. What is perceptual distortion and how may it arise?

(Suggested Answers are at the end.)

Improving Health and Safety Behaviour

IN THIS SECTION...

- Safety-related behaviour in an organisation can only be improved if a clear commitment has been made by management, with visible leadership.
- Competent staff have the appropriate training, skills, experience and knowledge necessary to do their jobs safely.
- Communication of safety information can be verbal, written or graphic and there are strengths and weaknesses associated with each method.
- Notice boards, posters, toolbox talks, memos and handbooks all have a part to play in delivering safety information to employees.
- Employers have a legal duty to consult with their workers on health and safety matters.
- This consultation is subject to two sets of regulations; one set applies in the unionised workplace and the other set applies in a non-unionised workplace.
- A health and safety committee is an important method for achieving consultation. To work effectively, the committee has to be set up and run according to agreed rules and procedures, which form part of the policy arrangements of the organisation.
- Training is a vital tool in improving safety-related behaviour and there are various occasions when training should be provided, for example, at induction.

Management Commitment and Leadership

Management commitment starts at the very top of the organisation. Senior managers must provide the leadership necessary to inspire and motivate managers at all levels to pursue health and safety objectives rigorously. This is done by establishing the organisation's safety policy with clear priorities and targets to be achieved.

It is also critical that middle and junior management follow through the commitment of senior management by means of the priorities and objectives that they set their staff. In this way, commitment is cascaded down through the organisation.

An important factor in demonstrating management commitment is visible leadership. If management are never seen taking an active interest in safety issues, then there will be an assumption that they are not interested. Individual managers must show their commitment to health and safety to their staff as this creates the local safety culture.

Management Commitment and Leadership

Visible commitment can be demonstrated by:

- Behaving safely (leading by example).
- Involvement in the day-to-day management of health and safety, e.g. by attending safety meetings.
- Taking part in safety tours or audits.
- Promoting changes to improve health and safety.
- Enforcing the company safety rules.

On the last point; managers must be able to recognise and enforce the correct safety standards. They must be able to praise and reward good behaviour and they must be able to challenge and correct poor safety-related behaviour. Workers must not be allowed to carry out their work unsafely without being challenged. If this is allowed to persist, management will quickly lose the ability to challenge any unsafe behaviour and will be unable to enforce discipline. This means that sometimes workers have to be taken into formal disciplinary procedures for failure to comply with safety requirements. Their behaviour may be so bad that this results in dismissal for gross misconduct.

Competent Staff

A competent person is someone who has sufficient training, skills, experience and knowledge (and perhaps other abilities such as attitude and physical ability) to be able to carry out their work safely.

It is the responsibility of the employer to ensure that workers are competent to carry out the tasks that they have been allocated. The more competent the worker, the better able they will be to do their job safely.

Managers should also be competent. This means that all managers should have an understanding of the health and safety implications of the decisions they make on a day-to-day basis. This is often overlooked. For example, if a manager is in control of a warehouse then they must understand the difference between safe and unsafe forklift-truck driving. They do not need to be able to drive a forklift-truck themselves, but they must have sufficient knowledge to spot good and poor behaviour when they see it.

Keeping Up to Date with Legal Requirements

Identifying and keeping up to date with legal requirements is an essential part of the planning process.

A basic health and safety planning process considers the three fundamental questions: 'where are we now?', 'where do we want to be?' and 'how do we get there?'. The answer to the second question; 'where do we want to be?' should always recognise legal compliance as a minimum standard to be achieved in the workplace. The 'where are we now?' process will then involve comparison with relevant legal standards in the form of a gap analysis to identify where legal compliance is not being achieved. This requires up-to-date knowledge of the relevant legal standards.

There are a number of methods by which organisations and individuals can keep up to date regarding health and safety legislation. These include:

- HSE website and HSE electronic newsletters (www.hse.gov.uk).
- Organisations and charities with an interest in occupational safety and health, such as the Institution of Occupational Safety and Health (IOSH) and the Royal Society for the Prevention of Accidents (ROSPA).
- Periodicals such as Safety and Health Practitioner (published online by IOSH).
- Subscription news and update services offered by private businesses, (e.g. Croners).
- Attending legislation update seminars and conferences.

Effective Communication

Communication can be defined as the process of delivering information from a sender to a recipient. To be truly effective, the correct information has to be transmitted, received and understood.

There are three principal delivery media for communicating information: verbal, written and graphic.

Verbal Communication

Communication using the spoken word, e.g. face-to-face conversations, meetings, interviews, training sessions, by telephone or over a Public Announcement (PA) system.

This is the easiest and most commonly used form of communication but there are various weaknesses associated with this method. If verbal communication is to be used to convey safety-critical information to workers, these weaknesses must be overcome.

Verbal communication at work

Limitations	Merits
• Language barrier may exist. • Jargon may not be understood. • Strong accent or dialect may interfere. • Background noise may interfere. • Recipient may have poor hearing. • Message may be ambiguous. • Recipient may miss information. • Recipient may forget information. • No written record as proof. • Poor transmission quality if by telephone or PA system.	• Personal. • Quick. • Direct. • Allows for checking of understanding. • Allows for feedback to be given. • Allows for exchange of views. • Usually allows for additional information to be transmitted by means of tone of voice, facial expression and body language.

Written Communication

Communication using the written word, e.g. report, memo, e-mail, notice, company handbook, policy document, operating instructions, risk assessment, minutes of meetings, etc.

Limitations	Merits
• Indirect. • Takes time to write. • May contain jargon and abbreviations. • Can be impersonal. • Message may be ambiguous. • Message may not be read by recipient. • Language barrier may exist. • Recipient may not be able to read. • Immediate feedback is not available. • Questions cannot be asked • Recipient may have impaired vision.	• Permanent record. • Can be referred back to. • Can be written very carefully to avoid use of jargon, abbreviations and ambiguity. • Can be distributed to a wide audience relatively cheaply.

Graphic Communication

Communication using pictures, symbols or pictograms, e.g. safety signs, such as a fire exit sign; hazard-warning symbols, such as a skull and crossbones found on the label of a toxic chemical; or photographs such as of a machine showing a guard being used correctly in the operating instructions for the machine.

Limitations	Merits
• Can only convey simple messages. • Might be expensive to buy or produce. • May not be looked at. • Symbols or pictograms may be unknown to the recipient. • No immediate feedback available. • Questions cannot be asked. • Recipient may have impaired vision.	• Eye-catching. • Visual. • Quick to interpret. • No language barrier. • Jargon-free. • Conveys a message to a wide audience.

Graphic communication

Broadcasting Methods

There are various ways of broadcasting health and safety information using the three media we discussed above. Each of these broadcasting techniques has its own strengths and limitations and so usually a mix of some or all of these techniques is used to ensure that essential messages are transmitted and correctly understood by all staff.

- **Notice boards** - should be "eye-catching" and located in areas used by all workers, e.g. rest rooms or central corridors. Notices should be current, relevant and tidily displayed. Cluttered, out-of-date, irrelevant notices obscure the messages being conveyed. Displaying a notice does not mean that it will be read. Typical contents might include: the safety policy; employer's liability insurance certificate; emergency procedures; identity of safety representatives and first aiders; minutes of safety committee meeting; accident statistics, etc.

One poster that must be displayed in the workplace is the "Health and Safety Law" poster. The example shows the poster displayed at RRC's Head Office.

It is a legal requirement under the **Health and Safety Information for Employees Regulations 1989** that this poster is displayed in a central location within the workplace where employees can read it. The poster has blank spaces for the details of worker representatives and other useful contacts. If workers do not work from a central location, (e.g. home workers), then a leaflet can be provided that contains the same information.

Example of the Health and Safety Law poster

- **Posters and videos** - used to provide safety information, drawing attention to particular issues and supporting the safety culture.

Advantages of Posters	Disadvantages of Posters
• Graphic and therefore avoid language barriers. • Can be eye-catching and generate interest. • Low cost. • Can reinforce key messages.	• Can quickly become part of the surroundings. • May be defaced. • Can trivialise important issues. • Rely on the recipient interpreting the correct message from the image.

- **Films or videos** - mainly used in training programmes and, if well made, can hold the audience's attention.
- **Digital media and Intranet – Toolbox talks** - short, practical safety briefings carried out routinely in the workplace, often presented by the supervisor at the start of a shift. They can be useful for generating awareness and discussion on safety precautions, but seen as dull or a waste of time if topics are irrelevant or poorly presented.
- **Memos and e-mails** - written notifications used to provide specific information about a single issue, such as updating procedures, drawing attention to lapses in practice, etc. There is no opportunity for feedback or questioning, so their use is really limited to issuing clear and precise instructions or information.
- **Employee handbooks** - used to set out the organisation's health and safety policy. All employees should be given a copy on joining the organisation and updates are usually circulated to inform staff of changes. This is a key document, containing information such as site rules, reporting procedures, emergency arrangements, etc. It is standard practice to issue this handbook as part of the worker's induction and to get a receipt as proof of issue.

Health and safety practitioners can use a variety of methods to hold the attention of attendees at safety training sessions – videos, group discussions, quizzes and activities can all be used in the workplace to good effect.

Co-operation and Consultation

Improvements to safety-related behaviour will only occur in an organisation with worker co-operation and involvement. If workers feel that they are being dictated to then they will feel little ownership of health and safety. Indeed, they may come to resent instructions being imposed from on high and start to actively oppose safety initiatives and improvements. This creates a negative culture and negative behaviour.

The most effective way to avoid this negativity and to actively encourage worker interest and ownership is to involve workers in the decision-making process. This is best done through the consultation process.

Consultation with workers will always require an employer to consult with his own employees. Sometimes, it will also require consultation with other workers such as contractors working within the employer's premises or undertaking work on behalf of the employer. The following section focuses on the legal requirements for an employer to consult with his employees. It is worth mentioning that alongside the legal requirement highlighted below there may be a legal requirement to consult with contractors, for example **CDM 2015** (see Element 1).

Employee feedback can also be gained through additional routes such as during appraisals, at departmental meetings, through suggestion schemes, employee surveys and via complaints.

Consultation with Employees

There is a legal duty placed upon employers to consult with their employees on health and safety matters. This legal duty is defined in two sets of regulations:

- The **Safety Representatives and Safety Committees Regulations 1977** – which cover unionised workplaces.
- The **Health and Safety (Consultation with Employees) Regulations 1996** – which cover non-unionised workplaces.

These two sets of regulations are broadly similar, though there are differences.

DEFINITION

CONSULTING AND INFORMING

Consulting - the two-way exchange of information and opinion between the employer and workers so that the best course of action can be agreed. This implies that the employer listens to the concerns of his workers and changes his plans as necessary.

Informing - providing information to workers in a form that they can understand and then checking that the information has been understood. The information flow is one-way and the employer does not have to take any notice of feedback.

An employer does not have to consult with employees on everything, but particular health and safety issues where consultation would be appropriate include:

- The introduction of measures affecting the health and safety of the workers.
- The appointment of safety advisers and specialists.
- Health and safety training plans.
- The introduction of new technology into the workplace that will affect health and safety.

The diagram that follows shows the rough outline of the consultation framework that exists under the two sets of regulations.

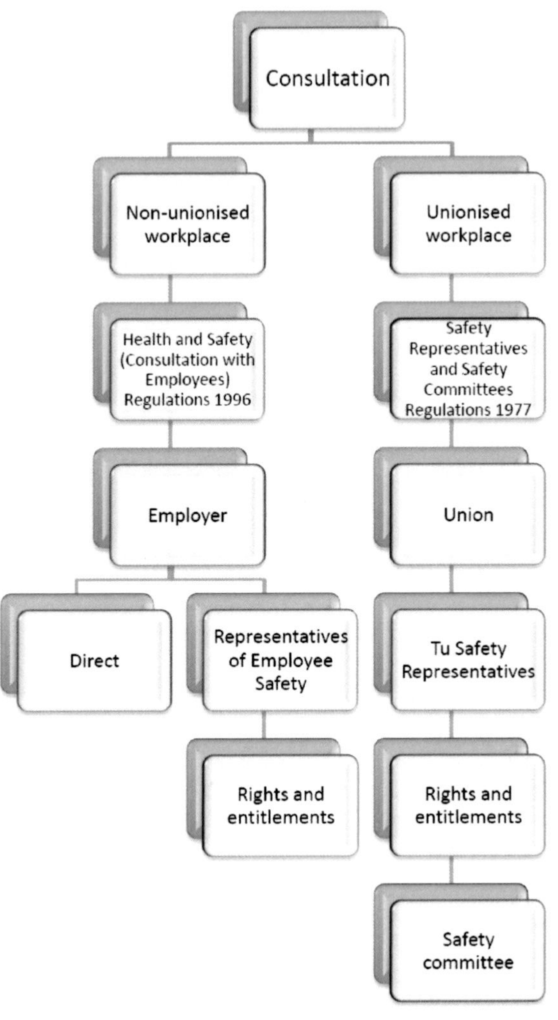

Consultation framework

Trade Union Safety Representatives

Under the **Safety Representatives and Safety Committees Regulations 1977** a recognised, independent Trade Union has the right to appoint Safety Representatives. These union members will ideally have two years' relevant experience. Once the union notifies the employer of the appointment of the Safety Representatives in writing then the employer must consult with them on health and safety matters relating to the groups of workers that they are representing (in effect; their constituency).

TOPIC FOCUS

Safety Representatives have a number of rights and entitlements, such as the right to:

- Carry out an inspection of the workplace (at least once every three months).
- Examine the causes of accidents.
- Examine and copy records and documents relating to health and safety.
- Receive information from HSE inspectors.
- Investigate complaints about health and safety.
- Make representations to the employer.
- Be consulted on health and safety matters.
- Time off with pay to perform their functions.
- Time off with pay for appropriate training.
- Reasonable facilities to perform their functions.

If the employer does not allow the Safety Representative to carry out these rights and entitlements then the employee can appeal to an Employment Tribunal. Safety Representatives are also given protection from being treated detrimentally by other employment law. They do not have any criminal or civil liability for health and safety standards in the workplace – for this reason they have "rights and entitlements" rather than "duties".

Representatives of Employee Safety

Under the **Health and Safety (Consultation with Employees) Regulations 1996** where the employer does not recognise a trade union for bargaining purposes, he can decide to consult with his employees directly or through elected representatives. If the employer chooses the latter route then these representatives are called Representatives of Employee Safety (RoES).

Consultation with workers

Once elected, RoES have very similar functions, rights and entitlements to their union equivalents with some notable exceptions; they are not entitled to carry out an inspection of the workplace, neither are they entitled to investigate the causes of accidents, receive certain information from inspectors or attend a safety committee. Of course, this does not prevent them from doing so with the employer's permission, but they are not legally entitled to do so.

Functions of health and safety representatives

Safety Representatives and Safety Committees Regulations 1977	Health and Safety (Consultation with Employees) Regulations 1996
Representatives:	
Appointed in writing by a trade union recognised for collective bargaining purposes.	Elected by the workforce, where the employer has decided not to consult directly.
Title/position:	
Safety representatives.	Representatives of employee safety.
Functions:	
Investigate potential hazards and dangerous occurrences at the workplace, complaints by an employee relating to health, safety and welfare at work, and examine causes of workplace accidents.	
Representation to the employer on the above investigations, and on general matters affecting the health and safety of the employees they represent.	Representation to the employer on: ■ potential hazards and dangerous occurrences; ■ general matters affecting the health and safety of the employees they represent; and ■ specific matters on which the employer must consult.
Inspect the workplace.	
Represent employees in dealings with health and safety inspectors.	Represent employees in dealings with health and safety inspectors.
Receive certain information from inspectors.	
Attend health and safety committee meetings.	

(Source: INDG232(rev2) Consulting employees on health and safety, HSE, 2013 (http://www.hse.gov.uk/pubns/indg232.pdf)

Safety Committees

Under the **Safety Representatives and Safety Committees Regulations 1977**, an employer is obliged to establish a safety committee when requested to do so by two or more Safety Representatives in writing. The employer must comply within three months.

An employer is not under a similar obligation under the **Health and Safety (Consultation with Employees) Regulations 1996**. However, since an employer is obliged to consult with RoES under these regulations, the formation wof a safety group or safety team is the usual route taken.

HINTS AND TIPS

You will note for non-unionised organisations we have used the term "safety team" rather than committee – in practice it can be called anything you like, but for an exam you should use the terms "reps and committees" for unions and "RoES and teams" for non-unions.

For the rest of this section references to the effective safety committee apply equally to any safety group.

The exact composition of the Safety Committee or safety team is a matter for agreement between the employer and the representatives. Members might include:

- Worker safety representatives.
- One or more operational managers with authority.
- A safety adviser.
- An occupational health nurse or doctor.
- Facilities manager.
- Human resources manager.
- Training manager.

Should an employer not wish to form a safety team under the **Health and Safety (Consultation with Employees) Regulations 1996** they are allowed in law to consult directly with their employees, which could be via appraisals, town hall meetings, departmental meetings, etc. However, the safety team is the usual route for many organisations.

TOPIC FOCUS

The Health and Safety Committee

This applies equally to any health and safety team or group.

To work effectively, the committee has to be set up and run according to agreed rules and procedures, which form a part of the policy arrangements of the organisation. The following issues should be taken into account in these arrangements:

- Who is on the committee?

  There has to be a balance between managers and workers and the right managers have to be included.

- How often will the committee meet?

  The committee should meet regularly and frequently enough to be useful, e.g. once a month.

(Continued)

TOPIC FOCUS

- Who will act as chairperson?

  All meetings need someone to take charge so that the discussion during the meeting is relevant, and to make sure that everybody has an opportunity to speak.

- What authority will the committee have?

  The committee must be able to make decisions, otherwise there will be lots of talk but no action. Usually, the committee will involve one or more senior managers who have executive authority.

- What will be discussed?

  It is common practice for a committee meeting to have a published agenda that has been agreed before the meeting takes place.

- How will the discussions be recorded?

  Minutes of the meetings are usually taken and then posted on noticeboards in the workplace for all workers to see.

- How will issues discussed be followed up?

  All agreed actions must be recorded in the minutes of the meeting together with the name of the person responsible for taking that action and a deadline. This action plan can then be reviewed at the start of the next meeting to check that the action has been completed.

The exact functions of the safety committee are not dictated, but should include issues such as:

- Studying accident and disease statistics.
- Reviewing the reports from active monitoring in the workplace such as safety inspections and behavioural observations.
- Examining safety audit reports.
- Considering reports and information from HSE.
- Considering reports submitted by safety representatives.
- Assisting in the development of procedures and policy.
- Monitoring the effectiveness of training.
- Monitoring the effectiveness of safety communications.

In this way, the committee is intended to be strategic, rather than involved in trivia.

Training

Training (in the context of health and safety) can be defined as the planned, formal process of acquiring and practising knowledge and skills in a relatively safe environment.

The Effect of Training

Training is central to the management of health and safety in workplaces. Employers have a responsibility to train their staff to carry out their jobs in a safe manner. Training is a key component of competence. In the absence of training it is difficult to develop or demonstrate competence and, as a result, statute law in many countries requires that an employer provides appropriate training for their workers.

The reason for this requirement is simple; training has a dramatic effect on safety-related behaviour. Without training, workers try to do their jobs to the best of their ability but they do so either by informally copying others (including copying all the bad habits and unsafe working practices that they see) or by doing the job the way that they think is best. Once the worker has been trained they will understand:

- The hazards and risks inherent in their work.
- The correct rules and precautions to apply.
- Foreseeable emergencies and the actions to take should these events occur.
- Identifying who to contact with any issues.
- Limitations and restrictions that apply to their work.
- Their personal health and safety responsibilities.
- The consequences of breaking the rules including disciplinary procedures.

Training Opportunities

Various circumstances require the provision of training:

- **New employees** - induction training takes place when workers join an organisation. This allows the worker to obtain knowledge about the organisation in a safe, structured manner and ensures that critical information is delivered and understood. Since a worker is at risk in a workplace from their first day of work, it makes sense to deliver induction training as soon as they start work and to cover safety-critical information, such as emergency procedures first.

TOPIC FOCUS

Typical content of a general induction training course for new starters includes:

- The organisation's health and safety policy.
- Fire and other emergency procedures.
- Details of specific workplace hazards and controls.
- First aid facilities and personnel.
- The location of welfare facilities.
- Safe movement around the workplace.
- Accident and incident reporting procedures.
- Worker consultation arrangements.
- General safety rules, such as no smoking areas.
- Personal protective equipment requirements.
- Introduction to the safe systems of work and permit systems.
- Introduction to the risk assessment system.
- Responsibilities of individuals.
- Disciplinary procedures.

- **Job change** – additional training is necessary when a worker's job changes in such a way that they are exposed to new hazards and risks. For example, a health-care worker whose job changes from being hospital-based to delivery of care in clients' own homes will need additional training, not in how to deliver care, since the service they provide has not changed, but in lone working. They will be at far greater risk when they go out into the community to conduct home visits as opposed to working in the hospital.

MORE...

www.hse.gov.uk/pubns/indg277.pdf

www.hse.gov.uk/involvement/index.htm

- **Process change** – when the way in which the work is done changes, workers may be exposed to new hazards and risks that require additional training. For example, when a different product is being produced on an existing piece of machinery, this may create new risks that require training in new safe operating procedures.
- **New technology** – new technologies adopted by organisations create different hazards and risks that workers may be unfamiliar with. The mass introduction of desktop computers, screens and keyboards is an example of new technology introducing new risk into workplaces. Training on the hazards associated with the use of this Display Screen Equipment (DSE) and the correct layout and use of the DSE workstation is now standard practice in many workplaces.
- **New legislation** – changes to the law governing a particular health and safety issue often create a need to train workers on the implications of the new legislation, perhaps because working practices have to change or simply to ensure an understanding of the law and its requirements.

STUDY QUESTIONS

7. What are the main merits and limitations of both written and verbal forms of communication?
8. How are graphic symbols (pictograms) used in safety communications?
9. What should be the first priority in induction training?
10. Apart from at induction, when should training be provided?
11. How can employees be involved in the improvement of workplace health and safety?
12. How must employers consult employees?
13. What rights do safety representatives have?
14. When must an employer establish a safety committee?

(Suggested Answers are at the end.)

Principles and Practice of Risk Assessment

IN THIS SECTION...

- Risk assessment is the formalised process of identifying hazards, evaluating risk and then either eliminating or controlling that risk to an acceptable level and is a legal requirement under **MHSWR**.
- A hazard is something with the potential to cause harm.
- Risk is the likelihood that a hazard will cause harm in combination with the severity of injury, damage or loss that might foreseeably occur.
- The main objective of risk assessment is the prevention of accidents and ill health.
- There are five steps to risk assessment:
  1. Identify the hazards.
  2. Identify the people who might be harmed and how.
  3. Evaluate the risk and decide on precautions.
  4. Record the significant findings and implement them.
  5. Review and update as necessary.
- Hazards can be identified using various methods such as, task analysis, legislation, manufacturers' information and incident data.
- Employees, contractors, visitors and members of the public must all be considered in the risk assessment process.
- Risk can be scored or rated using a simple **Risk = Likelihood × Severity** calculation where likelihood and severity are allocated numbers on a scale.
- If the risk is unacceptable then controls must be introduced based on the general hierarchy of control:
  - Elimination.
  - Substitution.
  - Engineering controls.
  - Administrative controls.
  - Personal protective equipment.
- Administrative controls include safe systems of work, permits-to-work and the provision of information, instruction, training and supervision.
- Safety signs are used to convey information and are categorised into five main types; all with a standard shape, colour and meaning. Pictograms should be used, not text alone.
- The employer must supply suitable personal protective equipment when necessary and must ensure that it is used.
- Legal standards can often be used to indicate what level of risk is acceptable.
- Assessments must be reviewed on significant change, after an incident and perhaps periodically.
- Sometimes it is necessary to focus risk assessment on a vulnerable person or group of workers such as young persons, expectant and nursing mothers, disabled workers and lone workers.

The main objective of risk assessment is the prevention of accidents

Legal Requirements

The **Management of Health and Safety at Work Regulations 1999** (**MHSWR**) state that:

- Every employer and some self-employed persons must make a **suitable and sufficient** assessment of the risks to both their employees and non-employees.
- The assessment must be **reviewed** and amended as necessary if there is reason to suspect that it is no longer valid or if there has been a significant change.
- The assessment must be **recorded** if the employer has five or more employees.

Many other health and safety regulations require that some sort of risk assessment is carried out. These are often referred to as specific risk assessments since they focus solely on the issue or hazard covered by the regulations. For example, the **Control of Substances Hazardous to Health (COSHH) Regulations** require an assessment of the risk to health of exposure to hazardous substances. In contrast, the risk assessment required by **MHSWR** is not hazard- or topic-specific and so might be referred to as a **general** risk assessment.

Definitions

Hazard

DEFINITION

HAZARD

Something with the potential to cause harm. This can include articles, substances, plant or machines, methods of work, the working environment and other aspects of work organisation.

For example, a lorry moving around a site road is a hazard because it might run over a worker. Sodium hydroxide (caustic soda) is a hazard because it is a highly alkaline chemical capable of causing corrosive burns.

Hazards can be broadly classified as:

- **Physical** – things which cause harm because of their physical characteristics, e.g. electricity, work at height, radiation, vibration, noise, heat, trip hazards, moving machine parts, vehicles, etc.
- **Chemical** – things which cause harm because of their chemical characteristics, e.g. lead, mercury, sulphuric acid, silica, cement dust, etc.
- **Biological** – living micro-organisms that cause disease and ill health, e.g. hepatitis B virus (HBV), legionella bacteria (responsible for legionnaires' disease), rabies virus, etc.
- **Ergonomic** – stress and strain put on the body through posture and movement, e.g. frequent repetitive handling of small boxes leading to inflammation of the tendons in the elbow joint.
- **Psychological** – things that have the potential to cause injury to the mind rather than the body, e.g. exposure to highly traumatic events that can leave a person unable to adjust to a normal life after the event (a condition sometimes referred to as Post-Traumatic Stress Disorder (PTSD)).

Note that a hazard is the 'something' that causes the harm. If an office worker receives an electric shock from an item of electrical equipment that has a damaged flex, then electricity is the hazard, not the damaged flex. It is electricity that causes the harm; the damaged flex is the failure in the controls or preventive measures. If the flex were not damaged then the hazard would still be present (electricity is still running through the equipment) but it would be properly controlled and the electric shock would not occur.

A wet floor is a hazard that creates the risk of slips

Risk

The likelihood that a hazard will cause harm in combination with the severity of injury, damage or loss that might foreseeably occur.

Risk can be described **qualitatively** using words such as 'high', 'medium' or 'low'. There will always be a degree of subjectivity to this qualitative description since the words represent one person's opinion of the risk level. Different individuals have very different personality characteristics and so two people may disagree on the level of risk inherent in a hazard.

DEFINITION 

RISK

The likelihood of potential harm from that hazard being realised.

Risk can also be defined **quantitatively** using probabilities and/or frequencies that have been derived from hard data. This type of quantified risk assessment is far more rigorous than qualitative risk assessment but is beyond the scope of this course.

Risk Assessment

Risk assessment is a process that people do automatically all the time. When you cross the road you carry out a risk assessment; when you drive a car you carry out a risk assessment; when you boil a kettle you carry out a risk assessment. But, of course, this assessment is normally done very quickly and without conscious thought or effort. If you are not very good at this process then you will not live long.

There are occasions in normal life, however, when you might become more aware that you are assessing risks. If you look after very young children you will consciously think about the particular hazards that present a risk to a child. If you start to take part in certain sports or activities, such as rock climbing or scuba diving, you will start to assess risks in your conscious mind rather than doing it automatically.

DEFINITION 

RISK ASSESSMENT

Risk assessment is the formal process of identifying preventive and protective measures by evaluating the risks arising from a hazard, taking into account the adequacy of any existing controls, and deciding whether or not the risk is acceptable.

A workplace risk assessment is simply an extension of this automatic self-preservation mechanism that has been formalised to meet legal requirements.

TOPIC FOCUS

The HSE has defined five steps to risk assessment:

1. Identify the hazards.
2. Identify the people who might be harmed and how.
3. Evaluate the risk and decide on precautions.
4. Record the significant findings and implement them.
5. Review and update as necessary.

Objectives of Risk Assessment

The aim of risk assessment is to ensure that hazards are eliminated or risks minimised by the correct application of relevant standards; to prevent workplace accidents.

In particular, the objectives of risk assessment are to prevent:

- Death and personal injury.
- Ill health.
- Other types of loss incident.
- Breaches of statute law which might lead to enforcement action and/or prosecution.
- The direct and indirect costs that follow on from accidents.

These objectives relate directly to the moral, legal and economic arguments we discussed in Element 1.

The Risk Assessors

Risk assessments should be carried out by competent people. In this context, the word competent would mean people who have sufficient training, knowledge, experience and other abilities. The exact training, knowledge and experience required will vary depending on circumstances. In some instances simply an ability to identify, read and correctly interpret guidance on a topic is sufficient. In others, a detailed understanding of background knowledge is essential to be able to correctly evaluate risk.

A risk assessment might be carried out by one person. This is not ideal in many instances since it relies on one person's opinion and judgment. Ideally, risk assessment will be carried out by a team. This allows for various views and opinions to be taken into account and so may result in a more successful assessment. The composition of a risk assessment team is not dictated, but might include:

- Workers familiar with the tasks and areas to be assessed.
- Health and safety specialists such as safety practitioners and occupational health nurses.
- Technical specialists such as mechanical and electrical engineers.
- Line managers responsible for the tasks or areas being assessed.
- Worker safety representatives.

Workers familiar with the tasks and areas to be assessed

The size and composition of the team will vary depending on the nature of the workplace and the complexity of the risk assessment process being used. Note that it is not necessary for all members of the team to be competent in the risk assessment process, simply for some or one of the team members to be a competent person.

The involvement of non-competent persons (those who aren't trained risk assessors) is useful for a number of reasons:

- Those team members may identify hazards and risks that might otherwise be missed (two pairs of eyes are better than one).
- They may ask questions and propose solutions that might otherwise not be considered.
- It allows experience to be safely gained in the practice of risk assessment.
- It facilitates employee awareness, involvement and consultation and hence enhances safety culture.

Criteria For a Suitable and Sufficient Assessment

A risk assessment should be "suitable and sufficient".

In other words, it should be good enough to fulfil legal requirements (**MHSWR**) and prevent foreseeable injuries and ill health from happening.

TOPIC FOCUS

A suitable and sufficient risk assessment should:

- Identify the significant risks arising out of work, i.e. those which are most likely to occur and result in harm being caused, with any remaining risks being at an acceptable low level.
- Enable the employer to identify and prioritise the measures that must be taken to protect people from harm, including complying with any relevant legal provisions.
- Be appropriate to the nature of the work and remain valid for a reasonable period of time. In other words, the assessment should be proportionate to the risks in the workplace.

To expand on this last point; that a risk assessment should be proportionate to the risks inherent in the workplace:

- A low-risk workplace with a few straightforward, often predictable hazards, (e.g. a retail shop), should have a relatively simple risk assessment carried out by a competent person (perhaps the manager) by reference to some basic guidance documents.
- A high-risk workplace, (e.g. a chemical works), should have a far more complex risk assessment carried out by competent persons (PhD industrial chemists, etc.) using detailed, complex reference material.

The first assessment might take a few hours to complete; the second might take weeks.

Identifying Hazards

The first step in the risk assessment process is to identify all the significant hazards associated with the work.

Hazards are the things with the potential to cause harm. It is important to identify both the **safety hazards** that might give rise to immediate physical injury and the **health hazards** that might cause disease or ill health.

Safety Hazards

There are many hazards that are capable of causing immediate physical injury and these can be categorised according to the type of accident that is foreseen:

- Work at height.
- Falling objects.
- Collision with stationary objects.
- Trapped/crushed under or between objects, e.g. a load falling off a forklift-truck.
- Manual handling.
- Contact with machinery.
- Electricity.
- Transport.
- Contact with chemicals.
- Asphyxiation due to a lack of oxygen/drowning in water.
- Fire and explosion.

- Animals.
- Violence.

Health Hazards

Some hazards can cause occupational disease or ill-health conditions. This can follow a single event (such as a needlestick injury infecting a worker with the hepatitis virus), but more often occurs as a result of prolonged exposure to the hazard over a period of weeks, months or years. These hazards might be referred to as **health hazards** and can be categorised into five groups:

- Physical, e.g. radiation, vibration, noise, extremes of temperature, etc.
- Chemical, e.g. lead, mercury, sulphuric acid, silica, cement dust, etc.
- Biological, e.g. hepatitis B virus (HBV), legionella bacteria (responsible for legionnaires' disease), rabies virus, etc.
- Ergonomic, e.g. very repetitive movement, stooping, twisting, manual handling, etc.
- Psychological, e.g. stress and trauma.

Exposure to high noise levels can cause noise-induced hearing loss

Hazard Identification Methods

There are various methods that can be used in hazard identification, such as task analysis, or reference to guidance, manufacturers' information or incident data.

- Task Analysis

  This is a useful method for identifying hazards, since it allows hazards to be spotted before work starts, rather than after the work has started. Task analysis involves breaking a job down into component steps and identifying the hazards associated with each step, so that the safe working method can then be established to deal with each hazard. This can be done before work starts as part of the planning process, and is how Safe Systems of Work (SSWs) are developed.

TOPIC FOCUS

There is a useful acronym for task analysis - SREDIM:

- **S**elect the task.
- **R**ecord the steps or stages of the task.
- **E**valuate the risks associated with each step.
- **D**evelop the safe working method.
- **I**mplement the safe working method.
- **M**onitor to ensure it is effective.

- Legislation

  Knowledge of the legal standards that apply to a particular workplace is an important aid when identifying significant hazards. For example, knowledge of the law relating to work at height will allow a competent assessor to identify which work might fall within the definition of work at height and which work could be ignored. Legislation is often accompanied by guidance documents which can be very useful in the identification of hazards. For example, guidance documents exist to spell out all the hazards that exist in engineering workshops.

- Manufacturers' Information

  When a new item of plant, machinery or equipment is purchased it usually comes with an instruction book that contains information about all the related hazards and instructions for safe use, cleaning and maintenance. Similarly, when a new substance is purchased, it comes with labels and a Material Safety Data Sheet (MSDS) that clearly identify the hazards of the substance.

- Incident Data

  Internal accident and near-miss data can be useful in identifying hazards. The main limitation here is that a hazard may be very significant but may not yet have caused harm in the organisation and may therefore go unnoticed. External data, such as national statistics published by the authorities, can be more useful since it identifies the real hazards and risks based on a much larger population size.

Remember that a risk assessment is a tool for identifying all the significant hazards that exist in a workplace - all the things that have the **potential to cause harm**. It is not a tool for only identifying those hazards that are poorly controlled. So, for example, in a new office with modern computer screens and keyboards, where someone has left a pile of boxes in front of a fire exit door, the hazards are electricity, use of Display Screen Equipment (DSE), fire and poor housekeeping. Not just the pile of boxes in front of the fire exit door, because that would ignore all the other hazards that exist in the office. In an office you are arguably at far greater risk from death by electric shock than death by boxes left in front of a fire exit door. The first assessment takes the electrical hazard into account, the second ignores it and therefore fails.

Identifying the People at Risk

When identifying people at risk, think not only of those carrying out particular activities, but also of those who may be affected by those activities. Individuals do not need to be named; rather, general groups or populations identified.

- **Employees** – may be directly involved with the activity, working nearby or passing by. Some hazards create risk only for the employee or operator carrying out the work, (e.g. a worker up a ladder is at risk from falling) whilst others create general risk for all employees, (e.g. a vehicle traffic route that all employees may have to cross in order to reach a staff car park).
- **Maintenance staff** – are often involved in the removal of the usual safeguards present in the workplace because of the nature of maintenance work, (e.g. the lift engineer who has to climb onto the top of a lift carriage in the lift shaft, or the engineer who has to remove machine guards to repair a breakdown). If the normal safeguards are being removed or bypassed, then risk to these workers increases and other methods have to be found to control this risk.
- **Cleaners** – may be exposed to greater risk because cleaning work may involve the removal of safeguards or activities that create additional risk, (e.g. window cleaning from an access cradle). Many cleaners also work alone, outside normal working hours, and therefore lone working also becomes an issue.
- **Contractors** – may be carrying out work independently of the work being carried out by employees or may be working alongside employees. The workplace creates risks for these contractors and the contractors create risks for the workplace. All these risks have to be considered through the risk assessment process.
- **Visitors** – may not be working but are still exposed to certain types of risk, (e.g. fire).
- **Members of the public** – may simply be in the vicinity of the workplace, yet still affected by certain types of hazard. For example, a release of toxic chlorine gas from an industrial site will affect passers-by and those who live near the site. In some instances, trespassers (uninvited visitors) may get onto the site. This is particularly important with regard to the possibility of children coming onto the premises, (e.g. playing on building sites or near railway lines).

In certain instances, identifying general groups of people who might be harmed by hazards is inadequate and a more specific focus has to be applied to a particular person or type of person who is more vulnerable for one reason or another. Young people, new and expectant mothers, disabled workers and lone workers all present these special cases (see later in this element).

Evaluating the Risk and Deciding on Precautions

Having identified a particular hazard and the people who might be harmed by it, the next step in the risk assessment process is to answer a simple question:

Is the level of risk generated by the hazard acceptable or does it need to be reduced?

The question may be simple, but the answer can at times be complex.

Likelihood, Severity and Risk Rating

Risk is a combination of the likelihood that a hazard will cause harm with the foreseeable severity of the injury, should harm occur.

Risk can be qualitatively described using words such as 'very high', 'high', 'medium', 'low' or 'insignificant'. The problem with these or similar words is that they are opinion-based and it may therefore be difficult to achieve consistent outcomes from their use.

An alternative approach that is commonly adopted is to break risk down into its two component parts and define each separately:

Risk = Likelihood × Severity

Then by the simple substitution of a word for a score it is possible to calculate a risk rating for a particular hazard.

For example:

Likelihood	Severity
1 = extremely unlikely	1 = very minor injury
2 = unlikely	2 = first-aid injury
3 = possible	3 = lost time injury
4 = likely	4 = hospital treatment
5 = very probable	5 = disabling injury

Using this scoring system the risk generated by a trailing electrical flex positioned across a busy corridor might be calculated as 5 × 4 = 20 (very probable × hospital treatment).

The same electrical flex trailing on the floor close to the rear wall of a rarely visited plant room might be rated as 1 × 4 = 4 (extremely unlikely × hospital treatment).

Note that in both instances the severity of injury is the same. This will sometimes be the case when the same hazard is being considered, but not always. For example, put the trailing flex in an old persons' care home and the foreseeable injury becomes more severe simply because the elderly have brittle bones and suffer severe injuries when they fall over.

There is no one right or wrong way to **calculate the risk**. Different organisations use different numbers and descriptions of likelihood and severity – some use a risk matrix, where numbers are used to describe the likelihood and severities, others use a "low, medium, high" categorisation. It is the general principle that is important here, not the exact words and meanings

The following graphic demonstrates how risk levels can be categorised using numbers and colour coding. In this example, green identifies a low risk, red identifies a high risk and intermediate risks are shown in between.

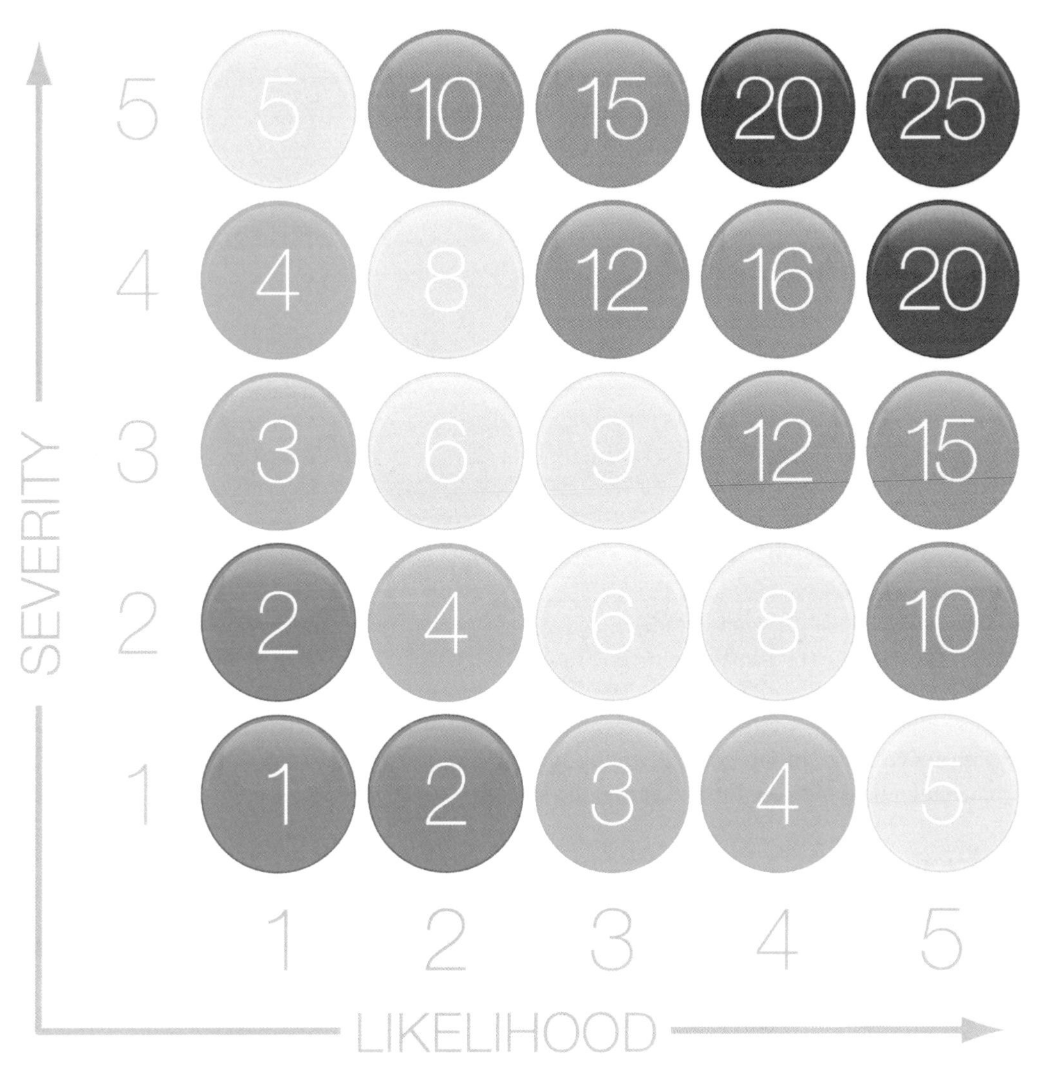

Risk Assessment Matrix

Using a risk rating system such as our example matrix above can be useful for several reasons:

- **Clarity of thinking** – people tend to think more carefully about likelihood and severity of foreseeable injury when they are asked to use this type of scoring system, giving a more accurate end result.
- **Consistency of approach** – different people can use this system and will get similar results.
- **Prioritisation** – since risk is now represented by a number, and the higher the number the greater the risk, it is possible to easily separate out the various risks presented by several hazards and rank them in order.

General Hierarchy of Control

When hazards are identified through the risk assessment process it is necessary to decide on the precautions needed to control those hazards to an acceptable level. This is the most important part of the risk assessment – identifying the further action that is needed and taking that action.When trying to decide what further precautions might be appropriate to a particular situation a useful approach can be to use a **risk control hierarchy**.

TOPIC FOCUS

The general hierarchy of control (based on OHSAS 18001):

- Elimination.
- Substitution.
- Engineering controls.
- Administrative controls.
- Personal protective equipment.

Each element is outlined in the following section.

Elimination

If a hazard can be **eliminated** then the risk created by that hazard disappears. This might be done by completely **avoiding** an activity that gives rise to risk. For example, an assembly workshop could stop welding steel in order to avoid the risks inherent in welding operations, and could buy in pre-fabricated metal components. The obvious limitation to this approach is that it is not possible to apply it to most of the activities carried out in the workplace. In this case, it may be possible to eliminate one or more hazards inherent in an activity. For example, hazardous substances can sometimes be replaced with materials which do the same job but present no risk to health (i.e. they are non-hazardous). Lifting equipment such as hoists and lifts can be used to completely eliminate manual handling. Machinery can be purchased which generates less noise to such an extent that there is no risk of hearing damage.

Substitution

Sometimes, hazard elimination cannot be achieved, but it is possible to **substitute** one hazard with another that creates less risk. For example, one hazardous substance classified as "toxic" (i.e. lethal in small doses) is substituted with one that is "irritant". The replacement substance is still hazardous, but far less hazardous. A handling aid such as a sack truck does not eliminate manual handling, but it does reduce the risk of injury associated with moving boxes around in a workplace.

Engineering Controls

Engineering controls involve the use of an engineering solution to prevent exposure to the hazard.

This might be done by:

- **Isolation or total enclosure** - the aim here is to isolate the hazard physically so that nobody is exposed to it. This might be done by total enclosure or containment of the hazard, e.g. total enclosure of a process which generates dust to prevent its escape; acoustic enclosure of a noisy machine to reduce the noise exposure of those nearby; guards around moving machinery to prevent contact.
- **Separation or segregation** - simply placing the hazard in an inaccessible location. An example would be overhead wires where an electrical conductor has been placed out of reach. In this case, precautions have to be taken to ensure that safe distances are maintained at all times, (e.g. the use of goalposts to warn plant operators on a construction site of the safety distances for live electrical overheads).
- **Partial enclosure** - for example, a hazardous substance might be handled in a fume hood or partial enclosure which the worker can reach into for handling purposes. Air is extracted from the top or back of this partial enclosure so that any airborne contaminant is extracted from the enclosure away from the worker.
- **Safety devices** and features that ensure that the item is used in the correct way and not an unsafe way. For example, interlock switches are fitted to movable guards on machinery to ensure that when the guard is open the machine will not operate (but when the guard is closed it will).

Administrative Controls

Administrative controls are those that rely on procedures and behaviour, such as:

- **Safe Systems of Work** - a safe system of work is a formal procedure which defines a method of working that eliminates hazards or minimises the risks associated with them. Safe systems of work are necessary whenever hazards cannot be physically eliminated and some element of risk remains. This applies to any task involving significant risk. There is therefore a specified routine for setting and detonating explosives in a quarry. The safe system is essential to prevent accidents or other incidents. Certain high-risk work activities may be controlled by a permit-to-work system (described later) as a part of the safe system of work.
- **Reduce Exposure** - if the degree to which a worker is exposed to a hazard can be reduced, then that worker is far less likely to have an accident with that hazard. For example, an engineer who spends all day working on machinery with hazardous moving parts is more likely to suffer injury than an engineer who only spends one hour of their working day exposed to the same hazard. The duration of each exposure, (e.g. for 10 minutes or for 8 hours) and the frequency of exposure, (e.g. once a week or 10 times a day) will both play a part here - the less time and the less frequently, the better.
- **Reduce Time of Exposure** - many health hazards in the workplace cause a degree of harm that is entirely dependent on the **dose** that a worker receives, e.g. the harm caused by noise, vibration, radiation and most hazardous chemicals (such as lead). The dose is determined by two principal factors:
  - The concentration, intensity or magnitude of the hazard present.
  - The time of exposure.

  For example, the harm to hearing caused by exposure to loud noise is entirely determined by the noise intensity (measured in decibels) and the duration of exposure:

  - If you are exposed to the same noise intensity for twice as long, it gives you twice the dose of noise; if you are exposed for half as long, it gives you half the dose.
  - The dose of noise determines the degree of damage done: the greater the dose, the more harm done.

  In all of the cases where harm is dose-related, limiting the time of exposure is an important control measure that can be practically used in the workplace.
- **Information, instruction, training and supervision, which we have covered already in this element.**

  Training is instrumental in enabling employees to become competent. A competent employee is equipped with all relevant information and is fully aware of the hazards and the use of appropriate preventive measures. One way that an employer might provide basic health and safety information is through the use of safety signs (see below).

  Supervision refers to management routinely checking workers and exercising their authority to control behaviour. Supervision, which is of critical importance as a management control, does not necessarily mean constant oversight of workers and the workplace. It is possible to supervise workers by making occasional contact with them at suitable intervals throughout a working period and it is possible to supervise workers remotely (i.e. from a distance).

TOPIC FOCUS

Safety Signs

Safety signs combine shape, colour and pictograms to convey specific health and safety information or instructions.

The **Health and Safety (Safety Signs and Signals) Regulations 1996** divide safety signs into five categories:

- **Prohibition** - directed at stopping dangerous behaviour, e.g. "No Smoking". The signs are circular with a black pictogram on a white background with a red border and red diagonal cross bar.
- **Warning** - tell people to be careful of a particular hazard, e.g. "Forklift Trucks Operating In The Area". The signs are triangular with a black pictogram on a yellow background with a black border.
- **Mandatory action** - instruct people to take a specific action, often relating to wearing personal protective equipment, e.g. "Eye Protection Must Be Worn". They are circular with a solid blue background and a white pictogram.
- **Safe condition** - identify safe behaviour or places of safety, e.g. "First Aid Station". They are rectangular or square with a white pictogram on a green background.
- **Fire-fighting equipment** - identify particular items of equipment, e.g. "Hose Reels". They are rectangular or square with a white symbol or pictogram on a red background.

PROHIBITION
No Unauthorised Entry

WARNING
Toxic Material

MANDATORY
Safety Boots Must Be Worn

SAFE CONDITION
Emergency Escape Route

FIRE EQUIPMENT
Hose Reel

Examples of Safety Signs

Pictograms must be used on the signs, not just text. This is to overcome any language barrier that might be created if text were used (as a result of illiteracy, learning difficulties, language or eyesight impairment).

Personal Protective Equipment (PPE)

There are instances where none of the above control measures can be used and there are times when some of them can, but residual risk still remains. If this is the case then it may be necessary to use Personal Protective Equipment (PPE). Many different types of PPE are available, such as:

- Ear defenders for noise.
- Gloves to prevent contact with substances hazardous to the skin.
- Respiratory protection against substances hazardous by inhalation (breathing in).
- Eye protection against splashes of chemicals and molten metals, mists, sprays and dusts, projectiles and radiation including bright lights.

DEFINITION

PPE

Equipment or clothing that is worn or held by a worker that protects them from one or more risks to their safety or health.

TOPIC FOCUS

Under the **Personal Protective Equipment at Work Regulations 1992** it is the duty of the employer to:

- Supply suitable PPE where risks cannot be controlled by other more effective methods.

  "**Suitable**" means:

  - It is appropriate for the risks and the conditions.
  - It is ergonomic (i.e. user-friendly).
  - It fits.
  - It does not increase overall risk.
  - It complies with any relevant standards.
- Ensure that when two or more items of PPE have to be worn together they are compatible.
- Provide suitable storage accommodation for PPE.
- Provide information, instruction and training to workers on the PPE they are expected to wear.
- Enforce the use of PPE.
- Replace or repair damaged or lost items.

The benefits and limitations of PPE are summarised in the table below:

Benefits of PPE	Limitations of PPE
• Can be used as an interim control whilst more expensive or difficult controls are put in place. • In some situations it may be the only control option available. • It may be needed as a back-up for emergencies when other controls have failed. • It is usually cheap. • It gives immediate protection.	• It only protects one person – the wearer. • It may not protect adequately if it is not fitted correctly. • It may not be comfortable and may interfere with the wearer's ability to do the job. • It may increase overall risk by impairing the senses, (e.g. goggles that mist up). • It may not be compatible with other items that have to be worn or used • People do not like wearing PPE. • If it fails it fails to danger (the worker is exposed to risk).

The controls options explained above are set out as a hierarchy: eliminating the hazard is the most preferred option and PPE the least preferred. The reason for this relates directly back to the human factors we discussed earlier in this element.

Workers do not behave in an ideal way in the workplace - they break rules knowingly and are subject to human error. Administrative controls and PPE are very reliant on personal behaviour and therefore are likely to be the least effective of all of the control options.

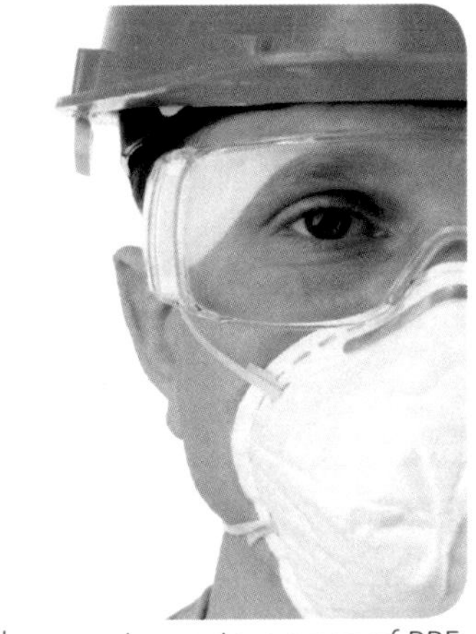

Worker wearing various types of PPE

Use of Standards/Guidance

The risk rating system described above is very useful as a practical tool for the day-to-day management of risk in a fast-changing workplace. It allows for a simple and consistent approach to the management of risk and the decision-making process. The one thing that this system does not allow for, however, is consideration of legal standards. If there are clear legal standards about the controls that should be applied to a particular hazard in a workplace, then the use of a scoring system and risk prioritisation and timescales, etc. becomes largely redundant. The only question that really matters is: Are we doing what the law requires?

In some instances there is a very clear legal standard that can be applied to the work in question. For example, the **Lifting Operations and Lifting Equipment Regulations 1998 (LOLER)** require that a thorough examination is carried out on lifting equipment. A risk assessment on a passenger lift should identify that the lift must be subject to a thorough examination once every six months or in accordance with a scheme of thorough examination developed by a competent engineer in order to comply with **LOLER**.

However, in other instances, there is no clear legal standard, or the legal standard is open to interpretation, perhaps because the phrase "reasonably practicable" is included. In this case, there will probably be Approved Codes of Practice (ACoPs) and/or Guidance published by the HSE and other authorities that clearly identifies the controls that are expected. Reference to the law, any semi-legal ACoP and guidance is, therefore, important in determining what the precautions should be for a particular hazard in the workplace. As was discussed in Element 1, ACoPs have special legal status; follow the ACoP and you will be doing enough to comply with the law. Fail to follow the ACoP and you have to prove that you did something else that was at least as good. Guidance has no legal status but can be very useful in understanding what the legal standard is and how to achieve it.

Residual, Acceptable and Tolerable Risk

Once control measures have been introduced and are taken into account, the current risk level can be estimated using Likelihood and Severity.

The risk that remains once controls have been taken into account can be referred to as the **residual risk**.

- If the residual risk is low then it might be considered **acceptable** - the controls are adequate.

  Nothing more need be done.

- If the residual risk is high, a decision has to be made about whether this residual risk is tolerable or unacceptable:
  - **Tolerable** implies that it is not acceptable but it can be tolerated for a short time with interim controls put into place.
  - **Unacceptable** implies that the risk level is too high for work to be allowed in any circumstances.

In the case of both tolerable and unacceptable risk, additional controls will need to be put in place to reduce the risk down to an acceptable level. Once these controls have been implemented a new residual risk level is created.

Priorities and Timescales

A straightforward link can be made between the level of risk associated with a particular hazard and the prioritisation of that hazard: the higher the risk, the higher the priority.

You might also assume that a high risk demands a short timescale for corrective action and a low risk can be allowed to persist for a longer period of time, but the problem with this simple link is that an inspector might not accept that a long timescale could be applied to a simple, low-cost remedy; it should be implemented immediately because it can be done immediately.

So priority and timescale are linked but they are not the same thing. Priority is the relative importance or urgency of an issue and will usually be linked to the risk level. Timescale is the length of time given for corrective action and must be decided based on the risk level and cost, practical difficulty, etc. of the control measure.

Recording Significant Findings

The significant findings of a risk assessment should be recorded to provide a statement of the hazards in the workplace, the extent of the risks that they present and the action taken to control those risks.

There is no standard format for risk assessments so different organisations can adopt a format that is most appropriate to their circumstances. Typical content would include:

- Identification of the activity/area assessed and of the significant hazards.
- Identification of groups at risk and those especially at risk.
- Evaluation of the risks and the adequacy of existing control measures.
- Action plans for implementing further precautions needed.
- Date of assessment and name of the competent person carrying out the assessment.
- Review date.

Reviewing

A risk assessment conducted under **MHSWR** must be reviewed and amended as necessary if there is reason to suspect that it is no longer valid or if there has been a significant change.

TOPIC FOCUS

Triggers for a risk assessment review:

- Significant change to a matter that the risk assessment relates to:
  - Process.
  - Substances.
  - Equipment.
  - Workplace environment.
  - Personnel.
- There is reason to suspect that the assessment is not valid:
  - Accident.
  - Near miss.
  - Ill health.
  - Change to legal standards.

It is also good practice to review risk assessments on a regular basis. This is often done by determining a frequency of review based on the level of risk associated with the activity in question. An annual review of risk assessments is common practice in many workplaces.

Special Cases and Vulnerable Workers

There are times when a risk assessment has to focus on one person or one specific group of workers because they are more vulnerable to particular hazards (or more at risk).

Young Persons

A young person is defined in **MHSWR** as anyone under the age of 18 years. The **MHSWR** require that they be given special consideration through the risk assessment process.

There are several reasons why a young person might be more vulnerable to risk in a workplace:

- Lack of experience in workplaces.
- Physical and mental immaturity.
- Poor perception of risk.
- Heavily influenced by peer group pressure.
- Eager to show a willingness to work.

For these reasons you often need to think more carefully about the work that a young person is doing. It may be necessary to:

- Prohibit a young person from carrying out certain high-risk activities, (e.g. operating high risk-machinery).
- Restrict their work patterns and hours (no night shift work or overtime).
- Train and supervise them to a greater degree than other workers.

Young people carrying out an experiment

Expectant and Nursing Mothers

Pregnant women and women who are nursing are more at risk from certain types of hazard. In most of these instances, the hazard presents a risk not only to the woman but also to the baby. Many of these hazards can cause miscarriage, birth defects or ill health in the baby. Consequently, new and expectant mothers are also picked out by **MHSWR**, which require that they be given special consideration through the risk assessment process.

TOPIC FOCUS

Hazards that present greater risk to pregnant women:

- Certain hazardous chemicals, (e.g. lead).
- Certain biological agents, (e.g. the rubella virus).
- Manual handling, especially later in pregnancy.
- Extremes of temperature.
- Whole-body vibration.
- Ionising radiation.
- Night shift work.
- Stress.
- Violence.

In all cases where a woman reports that she is pregnant, a risk assessment should be carried out focusing on the work that she is doing and the hazards that might increase risk to her and the child. It may then be necessary to:

- Change the type of work or the way that it is done.
- Change the hours of work.
- Suspend the woman from the workplace on full pay.

See the section on **MHSWR** in Element 1 for more information.

There are other employment and anti-discrimination laws that should be considered, but that is beyond the scope of this course.

Note that in certain rare instances it may be necessary to prohibit all women of child-bearing capacity from certain types of work, (e.g. handling certain types of chemical that are toxic to reproduction), on the basis that any exposure may cause harm.

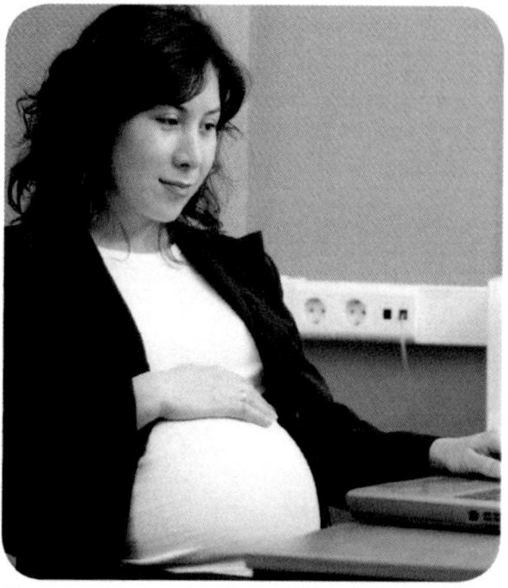

Pregnant woman working in an office

MORE... www.

www.hse.gov.uk/risk/index.htm

Disabled Workers

People with disabilities may be at greater risk from particular hazards depending on the nature and extent of their disability. For example, a visually-impaired worker may be able to carry out a packaging operation at their workstation without any risk to themselves or others, but they may find it very difficult to evacuate from the building during a fire using an escape route that is unfamiliar to them. In this instance they may need some assistance in the form of an 'evacuation buddy'.

During the risk assessment process it may be necessary to:

- Identify certain health and fitness criteria for some jobs and then screen staff against these criteria. This may have the effect of excluding those with a certain disability from doing these jobs, (e.g. forklift truck drivers should have their eyesight checked before being allowed to drive).
- Identify workers with known disabilities and consider what the implications of their particular type and level of disability might be.

Again, remember that there is other employment and anti-discrimination legislation that should be considered at the same time as any relevant health and safety law.

Lone Workers

People who work entirely on their own for periods of time, or those who are not alone but are not with colleagues whom they can rely on for help, might be classified as lone workers. For example, a service engineer who spends four hours alone in a plant room servicing machinery is a lone worker; but so is a health care worker who travels around in the local community visiting elderly patients to provide care (even though they may be in sight of other people at all times during their working day).

Lone workers are a group of workers who are especially vulnerable in certain instances:

- They may be more at risk of violence, particularly if the worker is exposed to members of the public, has to travel out into the community or is involved in work that brings them into contact with violent people, (e.g. prison staff or mental health nurses).
- They may be more at risk if they are injured or fall ill. Certain types of work involve a high risk of personal injury or ill health, (e.g. confined space entry). In these situations, lone working may be inappropriate or additional precautions may be necessary to protect the individual.

We will discuss precautions that might be adopted to safeguard lone workers in more detail later in this element.

STUDY QUESTIONS

15. Why is the distinction between hazards and risks so important to health and safety management?
16. State the purpose and objectives of risk assessment.
17. What techniques are used for identifying hazards?
18. What are the five categories of a health hazard?
19. State the five steps involved in risk assessment.
20. Apart from operators, what particular staff groups require special consideration during a risk assessment?
21. What factors are used to evaluate risk?
22. What is residual risk?
23. State the general hierarchy of control.
24. What conditions might trigger a risk assessment review?
25. What type of sign is represented by the following pictograms?

26. When should personal protective equipment be used?

(Suggested Answers are at the end.)

The Principles of Prevention and a Hierarchy of Control

IN THIS SECTION...

There are some general principles of prevention that can be applied to hazards in the workplace. These principles are listed in Schedule 1 to **MHSWR** and rely on the selection of technical, procedural and behavioural controls.

Introduction

All workplaces have hazards and all hazards create risk.

Good safety management is the logical process of identifying the significant hazards, evaluating the risk created by each and then either eliminating the risk entirely or reducing it to an acceptable standard by the introduction of controls where necessary.

General Principles of Prevention

There are some general principles of prevention that must be applied to eliminate hazards and reduce risk. Regulation 4 of **MHSWR** states that in implementing any preventive and protective measures, the employer must do so on the basis of the principles of prevention listed in Schedule 1.

These principles are:

Combat risks at source

- **Avoid risks** – where possible.
- **Evaluate risks which cannot be avoided** – through the risk assessment process.
- **Combat risks at source** – by going to the source of the problem directly, (e.g. if there is a noise hazard in the workplace, tackle the source of the noise).
- **Adapt work to suit the individual**, especially with regards to design of workplace, the choice of work equipment, and the choice of working and production methods, with a view, in particular, to alleviating monotonous work and work at a predetermined work-rate and to reducing their effect on health – this means applying good ergonomic principles to job and workplace design, (e.g. if people are becoming fatigued when carrying out repetitive work, introduce job rotation).
- **Adapt to technical progress** – by taking advantage of new technology as it becomes available, (e.g. buy mobile phones for lone workers).
- **Replace the dangerous with the non-dangerous or less dangerous** – by substituting one hazard with something else which is less hazardous, (e.g. replace a corrosive chemical with one that does the same job but is classified as "irritant" and therefore less harmful).
- **Develop a coherent overall prevention policy** – which covers technology, organisation of work, working conditions, social relationships and the influence of factors relating to the working environment; this means that a holistic approach must be used where the whole system of work is used to control risk, not just one single element.

- **Give priority to collective protective measures over individual protective measures** – by creating a workplace that is safe for all rather than relying on measures that only protect one worker at a time, (e.g. install a guard rail rather than relying on PPE).
- **Give appropriate instructions to employees** – so that workers have the necessary information and direction to behave correctly in the workplace.

TOPIC FOCUS

Collective protective measures are those which protect the whole workplace and everyone who works there, as opposed to individual ones which protect single individuals. These two approaches give rise to the concept of the safe place and safe person approach to managing safely:

- **Safe place** – the environment of the workplace, where the emphasis is on collective protection through the correct design, selection and engineering of premises, plant, machinery, equipment, processes and substances.
- **Safe person** – individual behaviour, where the emphasis is on the competence of workers who have received adequate information, instruction and training and follow safe systems of work (including the use of PPE).

These principles of prevention do not constitute a hierarchy. Rather, they are guidelines on the way in which employers should approach the prevention and control of risks.

When selecting control options from these principles of prevention you should remember that human factors have a part to play in effective health and safety management. So it might be expected that a technical control will be more effective than a procedural one, and that a procedural control will in turn be more effective than one that relies on behaviour. This is where the general hierarchy of control outlined in the previous section comes in useful.

STUDY QUESTION

27. Which general principles of prevention are not included in the following list?

    - Avoiding risks (wherever possible).
    - Evaluating risks that cannot be avoided by carrying out a risk assessment.
    - Adapting work to the requirements of the individual.
    - Adapting to technical progress.
    - Replacing the dangerous by the non-dangerous or less dangerous.
    - Developing a coherent overall prevention policy.

(Suggested Answer is at the end.)

Sources of Information on Health and Safety

IN THIS SECTION...

There are many sources of information on health and safety. Some of these are internal to an organisation, e.g. accident records, while others are external to an organisation, e.g. material safety data sheets provided by a chemical manufacturer.

Health and safety can be surprisingly complex. There is a wealth of information available which may need to be consulted. This information comes from two principal sources – those internal and those external to the organisation.

Internal Information Sources

Internal information sources give an insight into the nature of a health and safety issue at a local, organisational level. Internal sources include:

- Accident records.
- Ill health data/absence records.
- Medical records.
- Risk assessments.
- Maintenance records and reports.
- Safety representative inspections.
- Audit and investigation reports.
- Safety committee meeting minutes.

Ill health data/absence records

For example, an organisation's accident records can give an insight into the frequency and severity of manual handling injuries that can then be used to tailor preventive and control measures in the organisation.

External Information Sources

External information sources are useful not only because they give an insight into standards, but also because of the 'bigger picture' that can be gained. External sources include:

- National legislation, (e.g. regulations).
- Approved codes of practice and guidance notes published by the HSE and other authorities (such as fire authorities).
- Standards published by the British Standards Institution (BSI) or European and international authorities such as the International Organisation for Standardisation (ISO).
- Manufacturers' information such as operating instructions for plant and machinery, and material safety data sheets from chemical suppliers.
- Trade associations, such as the Chemical Industries Association.Safety journals and magazines.
- International bodies and agencies such as the European Union (EU) and International Labour Organisation (ILO) which set international law.
- International, European and British standards.
- IT sources such as internet search engines.

For example, a small organisation may not fully appreciate the hazards and risks inherent in a work activity, such as work at height, because that activity has been carried out by the organisation without incident over many years. However, reference to the HSE and the national statistics relating to work at height may change the perspective of the organisation by revealing the full extent of the frequency and severity of injury on a national scale.

MORE...

The Health and Safety Executive (UK):
www.hse.gov.uk

The European Agency for Safety and Health at Work (EU):
osha.europa.eu/en

The International Labour Organisation (UN):
www.ilo.org

The Occupational Safety and Health Administration (USA):
www.osha.gov

Worksafe (Western Australia):
www.safetyline.wa.gov.au

STUDY QUESTION

28. Identify two internal and two external sources of information about health and safety.

(Suggested Answer is at the end.)

Safe Systems of Work

IN THIS SECTION...

- A safe system of work is a formal procedure based on a systematic examination of work in order to identify the hazards. It defines safe methods of working which eliminate those hazards or minimise the risks associated with them.
- It is the responsibility of the employer to develop safe systems of work with the involvement of both competent persons and employees who will be carrying out the work. These safe systems must be documented.
- Safe systems of work are usually developed using the process of task analysis, which involves breaking work down into a series of steps so that hazards can be identified and risk controlled at each step using technical, procedural and behavioural controls. Once developed, safe systems must be implemented and monitored to ensure continued effectiveness.
- Confined space entry, lone working and travelling abroad are typical work activities that will be subject to safe systems of work.

Introduction

A Safe System of Work (SSW) is a formal procedure based on a systematic examination of work in order to identify the hazards. It defines safe methods of working which eliminate those hazards or minimise the risks associated with them.

We can identify three key elements from this definition of a safe system of work:

- The SSW is **formal** – documented or recorded in some way.
- It results from **a systematic examination of work in order to identify the hazards** – it is the result of risk assessment.
- It **defines safe methods** – it is the safe procedure or work instruction.

So simply put, the employer should carry out a systematic risk assessment, identify the hazards and precautions necessary and then formally record the safe way to carry out the task taking this all into account.

The Responsibilities of the Employer

It is the responsibility of the employer to ensure that safe systems of work are available for all work activities that create significant risk, just as it is the responsibility of the employer to carry out risk assessment of all work activities. Safe systems of work become particularly important when significant residual risk remains after control measures have been introduced into work processes. They are also particularly important when the normal control measures present in the workplace are removed, as often happens during maintenance work, cleaning or construction work.

The provision of SSWs is a part of the employer's duty under Section 2 of **HSWA**. They are also sometimes specifically mentioned in certain regulations (such as the **Confined Spaces Regulations 1997**, outlined later).

A safe system of work is the responsibility of the employer

The Role of Competent Persons

Safe systems of work should be developed by people with the relevant knowledge, experience, training and skills to understand the work under analysis. This implies that the people responsible for SSW development must be competent. In the absence of competence, key hazards may be missed and key risks not addressed. This might result in a flawed SSW that does not actually control the risk to an acceptable level.

Employee Involvement

The competent person must work closely with the employees who will be doing the work. The workers involved should take an active part in all stages of both the development and review of safe systems of work. Their practical knowledge and skills provide a valuable source of information about the nature of the risks, including unusual ones, and methods of working. They can also contribute by assessing plans and written documentation, and providing feedback on the effectiveness of the system in practice.

Involvement in this way enables employees to gain a deeper understanding of the hazards and risks, and of the way in which the safe system of work will minimise those risks. This helps to give ownership of the safe working methods to workers and to develop a positive safety culture.

Written Procedures

Documenting SSWs provides a precise reference for all workers, and ensures consistency of method. It also provides a reference for use in training and instruction in safe procedures. The recording of SSWs may be in the form of short notes, or perhaps manuals detailing exactly what steps to take when carrying out more complex and lengthy procedures, such as calibrating and setting up grinding wheels. SSW documentation can be accompanied by checklists for employees to use as aids to ensure that all the correct steps are taken, and to check off details before continuing with the next step or starting operations. Written SSWs also provide the employer with a written record which may be required for legal reasons.

Technical, Procedural and Behavioural Controls

A safe system of work will involve all the elements of control that we identified earlier in the general hierarchy of controls:

- **Technical, or engineering, controls** - applied directly to the hazard in order to minimise the risk. This may involve fencing or barriers of different kinds to isolate workers from the hazard as far as possible, or fail-safe devices designed into equipment to stop its operation if there is a fault.
- **Procedural controls** - the way in which work should be carried out in relation to the hazard. They will specify the exact tasks involved, their sequence and the safety actions and checks which have to be taken. Often, procedures will relate to the correct operation of technical controls.
- **Behavioural controls** - how the individual worker acts in relation to the hazard. They include general points of good practice in the workplace, e.g. good housekeeping, and specific measures, such as the use of PPE.

Development of a Safe System of Work

Safe systems of work are developed by task analysis, prior to work commencing, as a part of the planning process. Task analysis is the process of breaking a job down into its component steps and then identifying the hazards associated with each step. A safe working method can then be identified to deal with each hazard.

TOPIC FOCUS

Factors to consider when developing a safe system of work:

- Details of the task or activity to be performed.
- Details of the equipment and materials to be used.
- Any information or guidelines provided by manufacturers.
- Number of employees who will carry out the activity and their level of competence and training.
- The history of any accidents associated with the activity.
- The adequacy of the control measures in place.
- Any relevant legal requirements.
- The need for consultation with employees regarding the SSW.
- Any emergency procedures that may be required.
- Systems for, and level of, monitoring and supervision.

Analysing Tasks, Identifying Hazards and Assessing Risks

Can you remember what the acronym **SREDIM** represents? We outlined it earlier in this element when we discussed hazard identification methods and task analysis:

- **S**elect the task to be analysed.
- **R**ecord the steps or stages of the task.
- **E**valuate the risks associated with each step.
- **D**evelop the safe working method.
- **I**mplement the safe working method.
- **M**onitor to ensure it is effective.

So, for example, a vehicle breakdown and recovery company might perform task analysis on the job of changing the wheel on a customer's car.

This analysis might identify the key steps of the task as:

Step 1: Park breakdown vehicle.

Step 2: Remove faulty wheel.

Step 3: Fit spare wheel.

Step 4: Leave.

The risks associated with each of these steps would then be evaluated. For example, at Step 2, one of the risks identified might be movement of the customer's car after it has been jacked up, causing it to collapse off the jack. Another risk might be that of being struck by passing traffic.

Introducing Controls and Formulating Procedures

Once the risks have been evaluated, the appropriate safe working method can be developed. In our example, one of the controls would be for the worker to check that the customer's handbrake has been firmly applied and that the handbrake actually works. Another would be for the worker to wear high-visibility clothing at all times.

Implementing the safe system of work is often more problematic than developing the safe working method, because implementation requires workers to adopt the new working procedures and use all the identified controls. As we have discussed in previous sections, people's behaviour can be difficult to control. One way of overcoming or minimising this difficulty is to consult with and involve workers in the development process so that they are able to raise objections and concerns at an early stage; they then have some ownership of the new methods.

Instruction and Training in the Operation of the System

A key step in the implementation of any safe working method is the provision of information, instruction and training. In some cases, if the workers have the competence to interpret and correctly follow new methods, simply informing them of changes to existing methods will be sufficient. In other instances, detailed theoretical and practical training will have to be provided to ensure that workers understand and can apply the safe working methods.

Monitoring the System

The last step of the task analysis process is monitoring; once the safe working method has been put into place it should be checked periodically. This is to ensure that the:

- New safe working method is being correctly followed and applied. If it is not, then supervision must be improved.
- Method is, in fact, safe. If it is not, then it will have to be reviewed and amended accordingly.

Specific Examples of Safe Systems of Work

Working in Confined Spaces

A confined space is defined in the **Confined Spaces Regulations 1997** as:

> *"any place, including any chamber, tank, vat, silo, pit, trench, pipe, sewer, flue, well or other similar space in which, by virtue of its enclosed nature, there arises a reasonably foreseeable specified risk".*

These 'specified risks' include:

- Fire or explosion.
- Loss of consciousness or asphyxiation arising from gas, fumes, vapour or lack of oxygen.
- Drowning.
- Asphyxiation as a result of entrapment in free-flowing solid.
- Loss of consciousness as a result of high air temperature.

Entry into a sewer - confined space entry

Note that a confined space has two characteristics:

- An enclosed nature (ventilation will be restricted and access/egress may be difficult).
- One or more of the foreseeable specified risks exist.

Note that a confined space does not have to be small; an empty oil storage tank can be big enough to play a game of football inside, but it is still a confined space because of its enclosed nature and the risk of fire, asphyxia and drowning (as a result of an inflow of oil or other liquid whilst people are working in the tank, e.g. an in-feed pump might be accidentally switched on).

TOPIC FOCUS

Since work in confined spaces is a high-risk work activity, there are some general principles that should always be applied:

- Do not work inside a confined space if it is possible to do the work in some other way.
- If confined space entry is the only way to do the work then a competent person must carry out a risk assessment.
- A safe system of work must be developed for the confined space entry.
- Emergency arrangements must be put in place as a part of that safe system of work.
- Confined space entry must be under permit-to-work control only.
- All personnel must be trained.

When developing the safe system of work for confined space entry, the competent person will have to decide on the appropriate:

- Level of supervision.
- Competency requirements of the people doing the work.
- Communication methods to be used inside the confined space.
- Atmospheric testing and monitoring before and during entry.
- Ventilation that may be required before and during entry.
- Removal of residues.
- Isolation and lock-off of in-feeds and out-feeds.
- Isolation and lock-off of electrical and mechanical hazards.
- PPE requirement for workers inside the confined space which may include respiratory protective equipment.
- Safe and quick access and egress methods.
- Fire prevention measures.
- Lighting that is suitable and safe to use in the atmosphere inside the confined space.
- Suitability of individuals in terms of body size and psychology.
- Emergency and rescue arrangements to cope with foreseeable emergencies.

Note that confined space entry is subject to the **Confined Spaces Regulations 1997**.

Lone Working

Lone workers might be defined as "workers who are separated from their work colleagues". Many people carry out their work in this way, perhaps all the time or on a regular or occasional basis, e.g. sales representatives; installation, repair and maintenance staff; cleaners and night security workers, etc. Note that a lone worker may not, in fact, be alone: they may be surrounded by people - such as members of the public or customers - but those people are not their work colleagues.

The hazards that a lone worker may encounter will be the same as those of their colleagues working together, but the risks may be higher because:

- They lack assistance to do the work if things go wrong.
- Communication with colleagues and management is more difficult.

TOPIC FOCUS

To manage the risks associated with lone working, a risk assessment must be carried out and a safe system of work developed.

Various control measures may have to be implemented in the safe system of work:

- No lone working for certain high-risk activities (such as confined space entry).
- Arrangements for remote supervision.
- Procedures for logging workers' locations when lone working.
- The use of mobile phones or radios to ensure good communications.
- Lone worker alarm systems to raise the alarm and pin-point the worker.
- Procedures to be adopted by workers when lone working.
- Emergency procedures.
- Training for workers in those procedures.

A typical lone working scenario is a worker travelling away from their normal place of work (perhaps to undertake some work at a remote site, or perhaps to visit a customer or client). In this situation, the controls outlined in the topic focus box above can all be applied through the risk assessment process.

Lone working is subject to the general requirements of **HSWA** and **MHSWR**.

A worker in a remote location uses a radio to ensure good communication

MORE...

www.hse.gov.uk/pubns/indg258.pdf

www.hse.gov.uk/pubns/indg73.pdf

www.suzylamplugh.org

STUDY QUESTIONS

29. Define a safe system of work.
30. How does involving employees in the development of safe systems of work contribute to strengthening the safety culture?
31. What is the difference between technical, procedural and behavioural controls?
32. Why do instruction, training and supervision form a part of safe systems?

(Suggested Answers are at the end.)

Permit-to-Work Systems

IN THIS SECTION...

- Permit-to-work systems form part of a safe system of work to control high-risk work activities, such as hot work.
- A permit system formalises the control of high-risk work to ensure that all the risks have been identified, all the precautions put in place and that appropriate information has been communicated to all relevant parties.
- A permit-to-work usually has four main sections:
  - Issue.
  - Receipt.
  - Clearance.
  - Cancellation.
- Permit-to-work systems rely on the use of paper permits, but ultimately they only control risk properly when correctly used.
- Permits to work are typically used to control hot work, work on live electrical systems, entry into confined spaces, work at height and some forms of machinery maintenance work.

Definition of Permit-to-Work Systems

A permit-to-work system is a formal, documented safety procedure, forming part of a safe system of work, which ensures that all necessary actions are taken before, during and after particularly high-risk work.

TOPIC FOCUS

The sort of high-risk work that would normally be controlled by a permit system includes:

- Hot work (involving naked flames or creation of ignition sources).
- Work on high-voltage electrical systems.
- Confined space entry.
- Work on operational pipelines.
- Excavating near buried services.
- Maintenance work on large, complex machinery.

The high-risk nature of the work is the key feature that these types of work have in common, which makes them subject to permit control. If the work is not carried out in precisely the right way then workers and others may be killed. It is the intention of the permit system to focus everybody's attention on the high-risk nature of the work to ensure that:

- The correct safety precautions are in place before, during and after the work.
- All the people who need to know about the work do actually know about it.

Operation and Application

A permit-to-work system is a management system that is supported by, and makes use of, permits to work (which are pieces of paper).

Permits to work are formal documents specifying the work to be done, hazards, and the precautions to be taken. The permit provides a clear written record, signed by a responsible manager or supervisor, that all foreseeable hazards have been considered and all the necessary actions have been taken. It **must** be in the possession of the person in charge of the work before work can commence.

TOPIC FOCUS

A permit to work has four main sections:

- **Issue.**
- **Receipt.**
- **Clearance/Return to service.**
- **Cancellation.**

There may also be a section for **Extension**.

To see how the sections work read further on in this section.

Permits are usually triplicate copy documents with a unique identification number for cross-reference purposes.

In essence, the permit identifies the hazards and controls needed to safely do the work and then passes the responsibility for the area from the site to the workers. On completion the workers hand the area back to enable it to be checked and normal work to resume. The sections of a permit to work operate in the following way.

Issue

This section of the permit defines the work, identifies the hazards and determines the necessary safety precautions.

An authorising manager must complete this section. This will require them to carry out a risk assessment of the work in order to identify all the relevant hazards and precautions. The manager must be competent to do this.

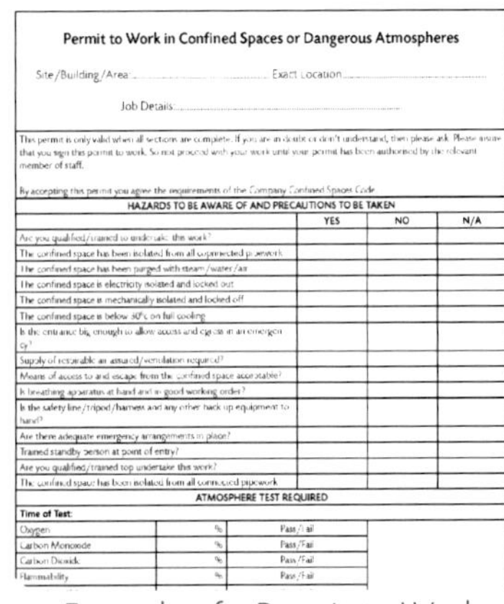

Permit to Work in Confined Spaces or Dangerous Atmospheres

Site/Building/Area: .... Exact Location ....

Job Details: ....

This permit is only valid when all sections are complete. If you are in doubt or don't understand, then please ask. Please ensure that you sign this permit to work. Do not proceed with your work until your permit has been authorised by the relevant member of staff.

By accepting this permit you agree the requirements of the Company Confined Spaces Code.

HAZARDS TO BE AWARE OF AND PRECAUTIONS TO BE TAKEN	YES	NO	N/A
Are you qualified/trained to undertake this work?			
The confined space has been isolated from all connected pipework			
The confined space has been purged with steam/water/air			
The confined space is electricity isolated and locked out			
The confined space is mechanically isolated and locked off			
The confined space is below 30°c on full cooling			
Is the entrance big enough to allow access and egress in an emergency?			
Supply of respirable air assured/ventilation required?			
Means of access to and escape from the confined space acceptable?			
Is breathing apparatus at hand and in good working order?			
Is the safety line/tripod/harness and any other back up equipment to hand?			
Are there adequate emergency arrangements in place?			
Trained standby person at point of entry?			
Are you qualified/trained top undertake this work?			
The confined space has been isolated from all connected pipework			

ATMOSPHERE TEST REQUIRED

Time of Test:

Oxygen	%	Pass/Fail
Carbon Monoxide	%	Pass/Fail
Carbon Dioxide	%	Pass/Fail
Flammability	%	Pass/Fail

Example of a Permit-to-Work

The authorising manager must specify:

- The exact nature of the work.
- Where the work can take place.
- The names of each of the workers authorised to carry out the work.
- The date and time that work can start.
- The period of time the permit is valid for.
- The control measures that must be in place before, during and after the work.
- Any restrictions.
- Any other permits that may be relevant.

The authorising manager signs the permit to formally confirm that all necessary precautions have been taken and that work can now start, provided the necessary precautions are adhered to. The manager's name and signature, and the date and time should be clear.

Receipt

Here, the handover process to allow work to start is formalised.

The workers sign the permit to formally confirm that they understand all the hazards, risks and precautions and that they will comply with all necessary control measures.

Names should appear clearly in capitals with signatures, dates and times.

Clearance/Return to Service

The workers sign this section of the permit to confirm that they have left the workplace in a safe condition, that work is complete and that normal operations may resume.

Cancellation

The authorising manager signs this section to accept the hand-back of the workplace from the workers.

This also has the effect of cancelling the permit so that no further work can take place under its authority.

Extension

This section is included in some permit systems in case there is any overrun of the work. It allows the authorising manager to grant an extension to the timescale of the permit.

Permits are often issued in triplicate:

- One copy is displayed in the area where the work is taking place.
- One copy stays with the authorising manager.
- One copy is displayed in a central location (often on a permit board) where other permits are also displayed for clear communication.

Remember that a permit to work is just a piece of paper; it does not ensure safety. What ensures safety is the management system that it represents. In some cases, permits are treated simply as unnecessary paperwork - to be filled in because someone at head office says so. This can encourage casual practices, such as authorising managers issuing permits without actually checking that control measures have been put in place, which can lead to unfortunate consequences.

A good permit system is only as good as the managers using it. To work effectively:

- Only authorised managers should issue permits.
- Precautions must be checked before permits are authorised.
- Permits must never be amended.
- The permit must be treated with respect.

Typical Permit Systems

Hot Work

Permit systems are commonly used to control hot work where naked flames will be used, (e.g. propane, butane or oxy-acetylene torches) or where a significant ignition source will be created, (e.g. welding or grinding operations).

Typical precautions for control of hot work:

- Flammable materials are removed from the work area.
- Items that cannot be removed are covered with fire-retardant blankets.

Cutting with an oxy-acetylene torch requires a permit to work

- Floor is swept clean.
- Wooden floor is damped down.
- A suitable fire extinguisher is at hand.
- A 'fire-watcher' is present in the area.
- The work area is visited routinely after the work has finished to check the area for smouldering.

Work on Live Electrical Systems

The high risk associated with working on, or near, live electrical systems means that this type of work is usually subject to permit control. In particular, permits are usually required for work on, or near, high voltage systems.

A permit system is used to ensure that:

- Working live is justified (i.e. it is not possible to work with the power off).
- All precautions are in place.
- The workers are competent to do the work.

Confined Spaces

Entry into confined spaces can be extremely hazardous, so should always be under the control of a permit-to-work system. This will require a competent person to carry out a risk assessment and then develop a safe system of work which identifies all the necessary precautions for entry and the emergency arrangements that must be put in place.

Machinery Maintenance

Maintenance work often involves the removal or disabling of safeguards and control systems. For large, complex industrial machinery, more than one person may be involved in the work and they may be required to work inside the machinery. This can generate high risk that might be best controlled using a permit system.

A permit system is used to ensure that:

- Work is carefully planned, assessed and controlled.
- The nature of the work is communicated to those who need to know about it.
- Power sources are isolated and locked off.
- Stored energy is released or secured.
- The workers are competent to do the work.

Machinery maintenance

Work at Height

Some work at height may be controlled under a permit-to-work. This could detail the area where work is permitted, the method of access (ladder, stairs, etc.), safe access routes and fall arrest precautions to be taken.

Information on a Permit-to-Work

Section	Contents
Issue	• Details of the work • Location • Date • Time/duration of permit • Hazards • Isolations or controls • PPE. Name and signature of authorised person issuing the permit
Receipt	Name and signature of person receiving the permit
Clearance/Return to Service	Permit signed back to confirm workers are finished
Cancellation	Permit signed to accept area back under normal operation and controls to be removed

STUDY QUESTIONS

33. What is a permit to work?

34. What are the four key elements of a typical permit?

(Suggested Answers are at the end.)

Emergency Procedures

IN THIS SECTION...

- An organisation should develop emergency procedures to deal with foreseeable incidents such as fire, bomb threat and chemical spill.
- These procedures should cover the internal arrangements for dealing with the foreseeable incidents, which will include:
  - Procedures to follow.
  - Provision of suitable equipment.
  - Nomination of responsible staff.
  - Provision of training and information.
  - Drills and exercises.
  - Contacting the emergency services.

The Importance of Developing Emergency Procedures

Despite all the controls that can be introduced into an organisation, things can still go wrong. Accidents and incidents do happen. When they do, it is critical that the organisation has emergency procedures that can be brought into effect without delay, otherwise there may be a poor or inappropriate response that makes things worse rather than better.

Clean up after oil spill

TOPIC FOCUS

An organisation has to develop procedures to deal with foreseeable incidents. Such incidents might include:

- Fire.
- Bomb threat.
- Spillage of a hazardous chemical.
- Release of a toxic gas.
- Outbreak of disease.
- Severe weather or flooding.
- Multiple casualty accident.

The foreseeable incidents will vary depending on many factors, such as the type of organisation and its location.

Emergency Procedure Arrangements

Having identified the foreseeable incidents, the organisation should make internal arrangements to deal with each of them should they occur. These arrangements should include:

- **Procedures to be followed**: in the event of a fire, for example, normal practice is for workers to exit the building using the signed escape routes and assemble at a designated place. In the event of a bomb threat, the procedure is often the exact opposite: to go to a room inside the building away from windows and external walls.
- **Provision of suitable equipment**: if there is a chemical spill, for example, absorbent granules or booms might be used to contain the spill and PPE used to prevent harm to those involved in the containment operation. In the event of a release of toxic gas, respiratory protective equipment may be needed.
- **Nomination of responsible staff**: in a fire situation, there is likely to be a need for fire wardens or marshals who walk through the building to check that everyone is aware of the fire evacuation; a fire team may also be required whose job will be to check the area where the fire is suspected to be.
- **Dealing with the media**: it is foreseeable that some emergencies will attract media attention. Procedures for handling the media should be developed and nominated staff trained in media handling techniques (such as how to answer questions from newspaper and radio reporters).
- **Arrangements for contacting emergency services**: while internal emergency arrangements must be made by the organisation to deal with foreseeable incidents, these responses will normally also involve contacting external emergency services for help. There should therefore be appropriate arrangements in place:
  - Communication equipment, e.g. land-line and mobile phones, satellite phones or VHF radio. The more remote the location, the more difficult this becomes.
  - Contact details, e.g. national and local emergency service numbers. This may involve international medical evacuation as well.
  - Responsible individuals with the necessary information and knowledge nominated to make the call. In many instances, the emergency services can provide a more effective response if they are given critical information quickly.

Training and Testing

Workers will only know what to do when these various emergencies occur if they have been provided with information and training. Any nominated individuals will require additional training on their roles in the emergency and on the safe handling of any equipment, (e.g. PPE) that they might have to use. Members of the public may require information on emergency procedures, which might be provided in the form of notices, or by means of public address system announcements.

Emergency procedures should be practised through drills and exercises to ensure that people are familiar with the actions they might be expected to take. In this way, people's responses become automatic. For example, fire evacuation drills should be conducted routinely in all workplaces and multiple casualty accident exercises should be practised in high-risk workplaces where they are a foreseeable event.

STUDY QUESTIONS

35. What is the main objective of an emergency procedure?

36. What types of incident may require the development of an emergency response?

(Suggested Answers are at the end.)

First Aid

IN THIS SECTION...

- An employer must make appropriate first-aid provision for his employees. This will include first-aid facilities and equipment, and appropriately trained personnel. He must inform his employees of these arrangements.
- To determine what first-aid provision to make, an employer will have to undertake an assessment which should consider various factors such as the hazards and risks inherent in the work, the number and work pattern of workers, and the geographic location and spread of the workplace.

Introduction

The basic principle of first aid is to keep the injured casualty alive until professional medical assistance can take over. This is sometimes referred to as the three Ps:

- Preserve life.
- Prevent deterioration.
- Promote recovery.

First aid also concerns the provision of simple treatment to minor injuries that do not require professional treatment.

First-Aid Requirements

An employer has a duty, under the **Health and Safety (First Aid) Regulations 1981**, to make appropriate first-aid provision for his employees. This is to allow an immediate emergency medical response to foreseeable injuries that might occur in the workplace. This provision consists of three elements:

- **Facilities** – an appropriate location where first-aid treatment can be given.
- **Equipment** – suitably stocked first-aid kits and other equipment as necessary.
- **Personnel** – staff with appropriate training to deliver first-aid treatment.

The employer must notify staff of these first-aid arrangements and, in particular, the identity of trained first-aid personnel.

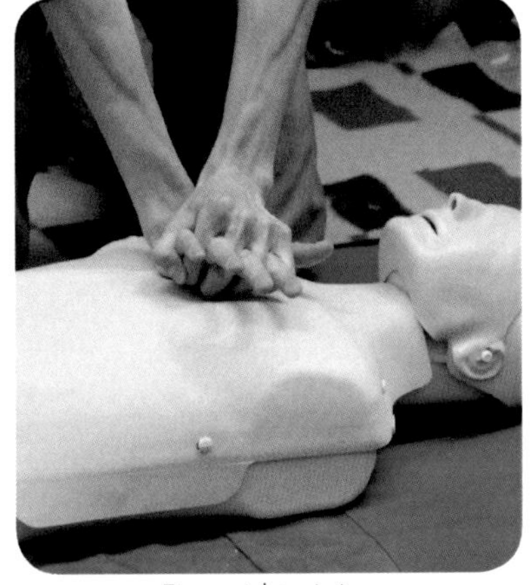

First-aid training

First-Aid Facilities and Equipment

First-Aid Facilities

Suitable facilities should be provided where first-aid treatment can be given. As a minimum, this might consist of a room that is used for other purposes but can be quickly converted into a treatment area. In a larger workplace, a dedicated treatment room should be provided.

This room should be:

- Centrally located in an area that can be accessed by the emergency services.
- Clean and adequately heated, ventilated and lit.
- Provided with hand-wash facilities, a chair and a clinical waste bin, etc.

First-Aid Equipment

As a minimum, one fully stocked first-aid kit might be provided for a small, low-risk workplace.

TOPIC FOCUS

The HSE provide suggestions on what should be included in a first-aid kit, for example:

- Bandages (preferably sterile).
- Sterile plasters (individually wrapped; appropriate to the type of work).
- Disposable gloves.
- Safety pins.
- Sterile eye pads.
- Unmedicated wound dressings (sterile; individually wrapped).

For more information see: http://www.hse.gov.uk/firstaid/index.htm

In larger workplaces, multiple first-aid kits should be positioned at various locations in the workplace, plus:

- Eye-wash stations.
- Emergency showers.
- Blankets.
- Splints.
- Resuscitation equipment.
- Stretchers.
- Wheelchairs.
- Other equipment as required.

The contents of a first-aid kit are covered by the ACoP and guidance to the regulations. Small travelling first-aid kits can be provided for drivers and lone workers.

Eye-wash station

First Aiders and Appointed Persons

Minimum provision would be a person available to take charge of the first-aid arrangements, which means looking after the first-aid equipment and facilities and calling the emergency services when required. Such 'appointed persons' should be available at all times while people are at work. Appointed persons are not necessary where there are adequate numbers of first aiders.

Appointed persons do not need to be trained as first-aiders, but it would be of benefit if they were trained to Emergency First Aider (EFAW) level. The status and number of first aiders will depend on a needs assessment.

Where the needs assessment shows there is a higher level of risk, first aiders (FAW) should be appointed in numbers appropriate to the risk and numbers of workers.

MORE...

www.

Information sheet GEIS3, Selecting a first-aid training provider - A guide for employers, HSE, 2013, available at: www.hse.gov.uk/pubns/geis3.htm

Leaflet INDG347(rev2), Basic advice on first aid at work, HSE, 2011, available at: http://www.hse.gov.uk/pubns/indg347.pdf

EFAW and FAW personnel must have suitable training and hold a valid certificate of competence. The HSE provides information to help employers select suitable first-aid training providers. The HSE also advises that EFAW and FAW personnel should have annual refresher training to prevent 'skills-fade', although this is not compulsory.

Selecting Staff to be First Aiders

There are a number of factors that should be taken into account when selecting persons to fulfil the role of a first aider at work. These include:

- Being reliable, having a good disposition and good communication skills.
- Awareness of their own limitations and limitations of the training.
- Having the aptitude and ability to absorb new knowledge and learn new skills.
- Having the ability to cope with stressful situations and accept responsibility.
- Physically fit enough to deal with the demanding nature of some aspects of first aid.
- Consideration of the need for first aiders considering gender, ethnicity and religious convictions.
- The person's normal duties should be such that they can leave their work immediately at any time to attend an emergency.

First-Aid Coverage

An employer should undertake an assessment in order to determine what first-aid facilities, equipment and trained personnel to provide.

There should be adequate first-aid cover on all shifts worked in the workplace, with weekend, morning, afternoon and nightshift work patterns all adequately provided for.

TOPIC FOCUS

Factors to consider when deciding first-aid provision:

- The general risk level of the workplace.
- The hazards present in the workplace.
- Accident history.
- The presence of vulnerable persons.
- The number of workers in the workplace.
- Work patterns and shift systems of workers.
- The geographic location of the workplace.
- The spread of the workplace.
- The need to cover holidays and absence.

The geographic location is an important issue to consider when determining first-aid provision. Workplaces within easy reach of the emergency services can perhaps provide minimal cover, but workplaces in remote locations, that the emergency services may take hours to reach, must be far more self-reliant.

STUDY QUESTION

37. What factors might need to be considered when determining the first-aid provision for a workplace?

(Suggested Answer is at the end.)

Summary

This element has dealt with the implementation of health and safety policies.

In particular, this element has:

- Outlined the duty of directors, managers and supervisors to ensure that their organisation meets its legal obligations. In particular, we looked at senior management's responsibility for planning, delivering, monitoring and reviewing policy.
- Identified how top management can demonstrate a clear commitment to health and safety by allocating adequate resources, defining roles and responsibilities, appointing a 'champion' at board level, appointing competent advisers and reviewing performance at board level.
- Defined safety culture as the shared attitudes, values, beliefs and behaviours relating to health and safety, and made a link between safety culture and health and safety performance.
- Outlined how safety culture might be assessed by looking at indicators such as accidents, ill health, compliance and complaints.
- Discussed the three human factors that influence a worker's behaviour: organisational, job and individual factors.
- Outlined the influence of a worker's attitude and motivation on their safety-related behaviour and considered the importance of perception.
- Looked in detail at some of the issues that must be dealt with in order to improve safety culture:
  - Clear management commitment with visible leadership.
  - Competent staff (training, knowledge, experience and other skills).
  - Communication of safety information in verbal, written or graphic form through the use of notice boards, posters, etc.
  - Consultation.
  - Training at appropriate times, e.g. induction training for new staff.
- Outlined the legal requirements for an employer to consult with their workers on health and safety matters, either through safety representatives or directly, depending on which particular set of consultation regulations apply to the workplace.
- Discussed the use of a Health and Safety Committee as a method of consultation with workers and looked at the various issues that must be considered in order to make a committee work effectively.
- Defined the terms hazard, risk and risk assessment.
- Identified the aim of risk assessment - to ensure that hazards are eliminated or risk is minimised by the correct application of relevant standards.
- Explained the five step approach to risk assessment:
  - Identify the hazards.
  - Identify the people who might be harmed and how.
  - Evaluate the risk and decide on precautions.
  - Record the significant findings and implement them.
  - Review and update as necessary.
- Considered that hazards can generate risk to both safety and health and can be identified by various methods, including task analysis, legislation, manufacturers' information and incident data.
- Outlined the groups of people who might be harmed, such as employees, contractors, visitors and members of the public.

Summary

- Discussed the principle of rating risk using a simple scoring system for likelihood and severity.
- Considered the importance of legal standards in the risk evaluation process and the idea that a general risk control hierarchy can be used to reduce residual risk to an acceptable level.
- Identified the three circumstances that might trigger a review of a risk assessment: significant change, after an incident, and periodically.
- Discussed the need to focus on vulnerable groups of workers such as young persons, expectant and nursing mothers, disabled workers and lone workers so as to further their protection.
- Considered the general principles of prevention that can be applied to hazards in the workplace.
- Noted the many sources of information on health and safety that can be used, some of which are internal to an organisation and some of which are external.
- Defined safe systems of work as formal procedures based on a systematic examination of work equipment and processes, to identify the hazards involved and define safe methods of working to eliminate or minimise risk.
- Identified the role of both competent persons and employees in developing and documenting these safe systems.
- Outlined the process of task analysis, where a task is broken down into a series of steps so that hazards can be identified and risk controlled at each step. This safe working method must then be implemented and monitored.
- Explained the relevance of safe systems of work to confined space entry and lone working.
- Outlined permit-to-work systems as a way of formalising the control of high-risk work activities.
- Explained the Issue, Receipt, Clearance and Cancellation sections typical of a permit to work and outlined the use of permits in the control of hot work, work on live electrical systems, entry into confined spaces, work at height and some forms of machinery maintenance work.
- Outlined why an organisation must develop emergency procedures to deal with foreseeable incidents, and looked at the internal arrangements that might be put into place.
- Outlined the need for an employer to make appropriate first-aid provision for employees to include first-aid facilities, equipment and appropriately trained personnel.
- Considered the factors that must be assessed when deciding on adequate first-aid provision.

Exam Skills

QUESTION 1

(a) **Explain**, using an example, the meaning of the term 'risk'. (3)

(b) **Identify** the key stages of a workplace risk assessment. (5)

Approaching the Question

Think now about the steps you would take to answer the question:

1. The first step is to read the question carefully. Note that the first part of the question asks you to **explain**, using an example, the meaning of risk. So you need to give a clear definition of the term risk. The second part asks you to **identify** key stages in a workplace risk assessment.

2. Next, consider the marks available. In this question there are eight marks so it is expected that around eight or nine different pieces of information should be provided. Questions that are split into parts (this one is split into two parts worth three and five marks respectively) are often easier to pick up marks on, because the signposts NEBOSH use are so much easier to see. In the first part, the question asks for an example (which will be worth one mark) and an explanation of risk for the additional two marks. The second part is worth five marks and there are five steps in a risk assessment, so it looks like one mark per step. The question should take around eight minutes in total.

3. Now highlight the key words. In this case they might look like this:

   (a) **Explain**, using an example, the meaning of the term 'risk'. **(3)**

   (b) **Identify** the key stages of a workplace risk assessment. **(5)**

4. Read the question again to make sure you understand it and have a clear understanding of risk and risk assessment. (Re-read your notes if you need to.)

5. The next stage is to develop a plan – there are various ways to do this. Remind yourself, first of all, that you need to be thinking about 'risk'. For the second part it might help you to think of a risk assessment you have seen or done, and the stages you or someone else went through. When you see the action word 'Explain', you need to give a clear account of, or reasons for the term being used. When you see the action word 'Identify', you need to select and name each of the key stages - this is a little more than a list. So, the answer plan will take the form of a bullet-pointed list that you need to develop into a full answer.

Your answer must be based on the key words you have highlighted. So, in this case we need to explain, with an example, the meaning of risk and identify key stages in a risk assessment.

Suggested Answer

Plan

Risk
• Severity × Likelihood = Risk. • Driving a car/van as an example.
Risk Assessment
• I/D hazards. • Who might be harmed and how. • Evaluate the risk. • Record. • Review.

Now have a go at the question yourself.

Example of How the Question Could be Answered

(a) *Risk is the likelihood that an unwanted event will occur, together with the severity of its consequences in terms of injury or damage. When driving a delivery van there is a likelihood that you may be involved in a road-traffic accident with other vehicles. The consequences of the accident may be damage to the vehicle, or injury to you or drivers and passengers in other vehicles. The risk associated with driving is therefore a combination of the likelihood of injury and the potential consequences.*

(b) *The key stages in a workplace risk assessment are to identify the hazards associated with the workplace tasks being undertaken; identify who may be harmed and how when undertaking those activities, remembering that this list may extend to visitors, contractors or members of the public; evaluate the likelihood and probable consequences of the harm that may be caused, assess whether the control measures in place are sufficient to reduce the level of risk or whether additional control measures are required; record the significant findings from the assessment; and carry out a review if new information comes to light, new processes are introduced, new legislation is introduced, an accident is recorded, or some time has passed since the assessment was made.*

Reasons for Poor Marks Achieved by Candidates in Exam

- Getting confused over the key stages in a risk assessment process.
- Not mentioning severity or consequences when defining risk, leading to quite a protracted definition.
- Defining hazard rather than risk - you must answer the question set.

QUESTION 2

Give reasons why workplace emergency procedures should be practised. (8)

Approaching Question 2

Think now about the steps you would take to answer the question:

1. The first step is to read the question carefully. Note that this question asks you to give reasons why emergency procedures should be practised. You do not have to explain the reasoning behind your selection.
2. Next, consider the marks available. In this question, there are eight marks so it is expected that around eight or nine different pieces of information should be provided. The action word is 'Give' so eight or nine reasons worded like bullet points will be sufficient. The question should take around eight minutes in total.
3. Now highlight the key words. In this case, they might look like this:

   Give reasons why workplace emergency procedures should be practised. (8)
4. Read the question again to make sure you understand it and have a clear understanding of why we should practise emergency procedures. (Re-read your notes if you need to.)
5. The next stage is to develop a plan – there are various ways to do this. Remind yourself, first of all, that you need to be thinking about 'reasons to practise emergency procedures'. When you see the action word 'Give', you need to provide your reasons without further explanation. So, the answer plan will take the form of a bullet-pointed list that you need to develop into your answer.

Your answer must be based on the key words you have highlighted. So, in this case, we need to give reasons why emergency procedures are practised.

Suggested Answer

Plan

Reasons
• Legal requirement.
• Internal policy requirement.
• Insurance company requirement.
• Vulnerable persons.
• Reduce likelihood of panic.
• Test communications.
• Identify weaknesses.
• Establish the alarm can be heard.
• Those designated to assist can practise skills.
• Familiarise employees with emergency procedures.
• Management commitment.

Now have a go at the question yourself.

Example of How the Question Could be Answered

Reasons why we must practise emergency procedures include that it is a legal requirement to practise fire drills. An organisation's own policy and procedures may stipulate that emergency procedures must be practised. It may be a requirement of the organisation's insurance company that emergency procedures are practised. Procedures should be practised where vulnerable persons are involved. Practising emergency procedures will reduce the likelihood of panic if a real emergency situation arises. Practice may reveal shortfalls in communication, either radio communication or verbal communication. Sounding the alarm in a premises will ascertain that the alarm can be heard in all parts of the premises. Practising emergency procedures allows those with special duties to also practise their duties. Practising emergency procedures demonstrates management's commitment.

Reasons for Poor Marks Achieved by Candidates in Exam

- Providing no answer at all, probably due to poor time management, and therefore achieving zero marks.
- Wasting time by giving two reasons (usually legal and familiarise employees), then going on to discuss the duties fire marshals may have. This is far too narrow a view and cannot attract many marks.

Element 4

Check

Learning Outcomes

Once you've read this element, you'll understand how to:

1. Outline the principles, purpose and role of active and reactive monitoring.
2. Explain the purpose of, and procedures for, investigating incidents (accidents, cases of work-related ill health and other occurrences).
3. Describe the legal and organisational requirements for recording and reporting incidents.

Contents

Active and Reactive Monitoring

IN THIS SECTION...

- Active monitoring is about checking to ensure that standards are met and that the workplace is in fact safe and free of health risks before any untoward event takes place.
- Safety inspections, sampling, surveys and tours are four active monitoring methods that can be used to check conformance to standards.
- Workplace inspections play an important role in ensuring that safety standards are acceptable in the workplace.
- Various factors must be considered when setting up an inspection system, such as:
  - The type of inspection.
  - The frequency of inspection.
  - The responsibilities for inspection.
  - The competence of the inspector.
  - The use of checklists.
  - Action planning for problems found.
- If an inspection report is written then it must be effective. This requires an appropriate writing style, structure, content and the use of persuasive argument to justify recommendations.
- Reactive monitoring is about measuring safety performance by reference to accidents, incidents and ill health that have already occurred.

Introduction

Health and safety performance should be monitored. This can be done using various methods that fall into two broad categories:

- **Active monitoring** – to ensure that health and safety standards are correct in the workplace before accidents, incidents or ill health are caused.
- **Reactive monitoring** – using accidents, incidents and ill health as indicators of performance to highlight areas of concern.

In most workplaces, both types of monitoring have their place.

Monitoring should be a line management function, but remember that senior management has responsibility for ensuring that effective health and safety performance monitoring systems are in place.

Health and safety performance should be monitored

Active Monitoring

Active monitoring is concerned with checking standards before an unwanted event occurs. The intention is to identify:

- Conformance with standards, so that good performance is recognised and maintained.
- Non-conformance with standards, so that the reason for that non-conformance can be identified and a suitable corrective action put in place to remedy any shortfall.

There are many different ways of actively monitoring health and safety performance. We will outline some of them in the following sections.

Performance Standards

In order to actively monitor performance standards you have to identify exactly which performance standard to monitor and what level of performance is acceptable. You could actively monitor the following activities to give a measure of performance:

- The number and quality of risk assessments covering work activities.
- The provision of health and safety training to schedule.
- The completion of consultative committee meetings to schedule.
- The completion of workplace inspections to schedule.
- The completion of safety review meetings to schedule.

All these management activities are likely to be taking place in the workplace, so it is possible to assess whether they are happening or not. In most instances, you can also measure the degree to which they are happening and perhaps assess their quality. For example, a standard might be that when contractors start new work on site there should be suitable and sufficient risk assessments to cover their work. The presence or absence of risk assessments can be checked. The number of risk assessments can be measured to quantify compliance and the quality of each risk assessment can be judged. In this way, a full picture of compliance can be built up.

HINTS AND TIPS

Note – "risk assessments" are not an active monitoring technique, but measuring how many were carried out vs. how many were planned to be completed is. Similarly, "training" is not active monitoring, but measuring the percentage of attendees who showed up for the planned training is. This is a subtle but important distinction.

Systematic Inspections

One popular way to actively monitor health and safety performance is to carry out systematic inspections. These inspections can focus on the four Ps:

- **Plant** – machinery and vehicles, as well as any statutory inspections and examinations.
- **Premises** – the workplace and the working environment.
- **People** – working methods and behaviour.
- **Procedures** – safe systems of work, method statements, permits-to-work, etc.

An inspection might concentrate on one, several or all four of these areas. Systematic inspection regimes usually exist in many different forms within different workplaces.

For example, in a distribution warehouse there might be:

- A daily inspection regime where forklift truck drivers inspect their own vehicles at the start of each shift – Plant.
- A weekly inspection regime where supervisors check that forklift trucks are being driven safely – People.
- A monthly inspection regime where the manager checks the entire warehouse for housekeeping – Premises.
- A six-monthly thorough examination of each forklift truck by a competent engineer to ensure safety of the load-bearing parts – Plant.
- An annual inspection regime for the storage racking to ensure structural integrity – Premises.

If this series of inspections is in place then it is possible to monitor the degree to which each is being carried out successfully. In this way, two different types of active monitoring are being carried out: one on the workplace directly (the four Ps), and one on the performance of those checks.

Safety Inspections, Sampling, Surveys and Tours

These are four slightly different methods of active monitoring, each of which has a place in an active monitoring regime. (Remember that the actual names given to these methods may vary between workplaces.)

Weekly inspection by a site supervisor

Safety Inspections

The term "safety inspection" implies comparison with a given standard, whether it is in-house or a statutory standard. Examples include:

- Routine inspection of a workplace to determine if general standards of health and safety are acceptable or if corrective action is necessary, (e.g. a quarterly housekeeping inspection in an office).
- Statutory inspection of an item by a competent person to fulfil a legal requirement, (e.g. the annual examination of an item of lifting equipment).
- Periodic inspection of plant and machinery as part of a planned maintenance programme, (e.g. a mechanic inspects the brakes on a lorry on a regular basis to ensure they are not excessively worn).
- Pre-use checks carried out by workers before they use certain items of plant and machinery, (e.g. start-up checks carried out by a forklift truck driver).

All these inspections can be repeated routinely to form an inspection regime, and can all be recorded to provide evidence of inspection.

Safety Sampling

This is the technique of monitoring compliance with a particular workplace standard by looking at a representative sample only. If a big enough sample is collected then there is a strong likelihood that the results of the sample will reflect the results for the workplace as a whole.

For example, if the standard in a large office complex is that all 1,200 fire extinguishers must be inspected annually by a competent engineer, then there are several ways to monitor compliance with this standard:

- Check the maintenance records to ensure each and every fire extinguisher has been signed off.
- Check all 1,200 fire extinguishers directly by inspecting every one.
- Check a representative sample, e.g. 50 extinguishers selected at random from various locations around the complex.

The last method is safety sampling. It provides better evidence of compliance to the standard than simply checking the engineer's maintenance records since they may have signed extinguishers off without ever inspecting them. It is also far less time-consuming than checking all 1,200 extinguishers directly – which is the job that the competent engineer had to do.

Safety Surveys

A safety survey is a detailed examination of one particular issue or topic, e.g. a detailed examination of the provision of emergency lighting within a building. The word "survey" can be used to refer to various types of detailed examination:

- A noise assessment usually requires that a noise survey is carried out by a competent person using a sound level meter.
- A structural survey is a detailed examination of the structural integrity of a building or item.
- A staff survey is an examination of workers' opinions, usually collected by asking staff to fill in a questionnaire.

All of these types of survey might be used to actively monitor safety.

Safety Tours

A safety tour is a walk-around in a workplace carried out by a group or team including managers. The group carrying out the tour should include managers from the area being inspected and possibly worker representatives, safety specialists, senior managers, occupational health specialists, engineers and workers from the area. One of the objectives of the tour is to raise the profile of health and safety and to demonstrate management interest and commitment.

Benchmarking

Benchmarking is the process of comparing performance against similar organisations or against national standards. Benchmarking can therefore be an active monitoring technique as it demonstrates progress.

Arrangements for Workplace Inspections

In many workplaces, systematic inspections play a crucial role in checking that the standards that should be in place are, in fact, in place. They allow management to resolve problems before those problems become critical. They also allow workers to see that checks are being carried out and perhaps get involved in the inspection process itself. Worker and senior management involvement in inspections helps to reinforce a positive health and safety culture.

Workplace safety inspection

Certain factors must be considered before the introduction of a workplace inspection system, including:

- **The type of inspection** – inspections are carried out for a number of different reasons and they examine different aspects of safety in the workplace. Is this a statutory inspection to ensure legal compliance? A general workplace inspection that looks at plant and premises? A pre-start inspection for an item of machinery?
- **The frequency of inspection** – likely to be determined both by the type of inspection and the level of risk. For example, a general workplace inspection might be conducted in an office once a month, but once a week in a workshop environment to reflect the higher risk. The frequency of statutory inspections is normally determined by the relevant law. Pre-start checks should usually be carried out at the start of every shift.
- **The allocation of responsibilities** – those responsible for ensuring that inspections take place should be identified, as should the employees who will be carrying out the inspections.
- **The competence and objectivity of the inspector** – an essential characteristic of whoever is conducting the inspection; the person should have the necessary training, knowledge and experience. In some instances, certification to a specific standard will be required; in other situations, all that is necessary is an understanding of the workplace, health and safety principles, and a willingness to ask questions. Training may be required for those who will be conducting inspections.
  A part of an inspector's competence is the need to be objective; they need to be able to recognise the facts as they are based on evidence rather than make personal interpretations based on bias or prejudice.
- **The use of checklists** – these are valuable tools for use during the inspection process. Checklists ensure that:
  - All points are covered by the inspector.
  - There is a consistency of approach to the process.
  - There is a form of written record of the inspection and its findings.

  However, checklists do have their weaknesses, the most important being that an inspector may only deal with the points on the checklist and ignore other issues that exist in the workplace but are not included on the checklist.

- **Action planning for problems found** – so that appropriate action is taken following the inspection to resolve issues in a timely manner. An inspection system that identifies a problem or issue, but then does not result in action being taken, is flawed. There must be clear identification of:
  - The corrective action that is required.
  - The persons who are responsible for taking that action.
  - Priorities/timescales.

The inspection system can be documented and formalised once procedures based on all these factors have been agreed.

Example Inspection System

A bank head office introduces an inspection system to actively monitor general health and safety standards. A set of formal arrangements is documented and included in the safety policy of the company. These arrangements describe:

- **The purpose of the inspection system** – to monitor general health and safety standards.
- **The frequency of the inspections** – once a month for all areas.
- **The persons responsible** – managers of a particular grade for ensuring that inspections are carried out, managers of the next grade down for actually doing the inspections.
- **Competence of inspectors** – the need for inspecting managers to attend a one-day course on the inspection system.
- **Inspection checklist** – a generic checklist is created appropriate to all office areas, which may be tailored by the inspector if necessary.
- **Follow-up arrangements** – an action plan table is created and included on the inspection checklist.

TOPIC FOCUS

Typical topic headings that might be included in a generic inspection checklist:

- Fire safety – including emergency escape routes, signs, extinguishers.
- Housekeeping – general tidiness and cleanliness.
- Environment issues – e.g. lighting, temperature, ventilation, noise.
- Traffic routes – safety of both vehicle and pedestrian routes.
- Chemical safety – appropriate use and storage of hazardous substances.
- Machinery safety – e.g. correct use of machine guards and interlocks.
- Electrical safety – e.g. portable electrical appliance safety.
- Welfare facilities – suitability and condition.

It is worth noting that you will be carrying out a workplace inspection in the second half of your studies to identify hazards and corrective actions as part of the practical assessment.

Effective Report Writing

Many inspection systems require the inspector to write a report summarising their main findings and recommendations. In some cases, this report is presented in a standard proforma style where the inspector simply fills in blank spaces on a report form. In other instances, a more narrative-style report is required where the inspector has much wider scope to explain and describe what they found and what they recommend should be done about it. If this sort of inspection report is written then it must be effective; this requires an appropriate writing style.

Writing Style

The language used in the report must be formal and free of slang and jargon. The tone of language must be factual and persuasive. The report must be concise. Busy managers do not have time to read long, rambling sections of text.

Worker completing an inspection report

- Structure

  A typical report will contain:

  - **Executive summary** – a concise overview of the main findings and recommendations.
  - **Introduction** – a few sentences to outline where and when the inspection took place, who was present and the reasons for the inspection.
  - **Main findings** – this can perhaps be divided up into specific topic areas. For each topic, the problem highlighted can be described in a factual manner and any relevant legal standard identified.
  - **Recommendations** – the immediate-, medium- and long-term actions needed to remedy each of the issues found should be identified, along with timescales and responsible persons. Actions should be prioritised on the basis of risk. Justification of the recommendations should be included.
  - **Conclusions** – a short section to end the report.

- Content

  The significant findings of the inspection should be presented. Trivia and minor issues should be omitted. The report must be factual and concise. Evidence of what was observed might be presented.

- Justified Recommendations

  Any recommendations made should be justified. A persuasive argument might be made based on the moral, legal and economic arguments.

  Recommendations might be presented in an action plan:

Recommended action	Priority	Timescale	Responsible person
Tidy the office	Medium	1 Week	Office Supervisor

- Emphasis

  Emphasis should be placed on the key issues – including trivia will detract from the main message and could result in issues being missed.

- Persuasiveness

  The report needs to be persuasive and drive the reader to take action, so use of the "moral, legal and financial" arguments for good health and safety standards can be used here.

Reactive Monitoring

Reactive monitoring uses accidents, incidents, ill health and other unwanted events and situations as indicators of health and safety performance to highlight areas of concern. By definition, this means 'reacting' after things have gone wrong. This indicates two weaknesses with reactive monitoring:

- Things have already gone wrong; things are being put right after the event rather than before.
- It measures failure; a negative aspect to focus on.

HINTS AND TIPS

There is often some confusion about the categorisation of "near misses" as active or reactive. Whilst they are responding before someone has been hurt, they are still "reactive" as something unwanted has happened, it just could have been a lot worse.

Despite these weaknesses, reactive monitoring is a valid tool for an organisation to use as long as some forms of active monitoring are being carried out as well.

There are two principal methods of carrying out reactive monitoring:

- Learn lessons from one individual event such as an accident, a dangerous occurrence, a near miss or a case of ill health.
- Learn lessons from data gathered from large numbers of events.

The first method involves incident reporting, recording and investigation (a key topic for later in this element). The second method is concerned with the collection and use of statistics.

Statistics

Data can be collected about a number of different unwanted events, such as:

- Accidents.
- Dangerous occurrences.
- Near misses.
- Cases of ill health.
- Complaints from the workforce.
- Enforcement action.
- Number and cost of claims.
- Cost of accidents, e.g. damage repairs.

This data can then be analysed to see if there are any:

- **Trends** – consistent increases or decreases in the number of certain types of event over a period of time.
- **Patterns** – collections or hot-spots of certain types of event.

This analysis usually involves converting the raw data (i.e. the actual numbers) into an accident rate so that more meaningful comparisons can be made.

One popular accident rate used to measure an organisation's safety performance is the Accident Incidence Rate (AIR):

$$\text{AIR} = \frac{\text{Number of accidents during a specific time period}}{\text{Average number of workers over the same period}} \times 1{,}000$$

(The answer is in units of 'accidents per 1,000 workers'.)

This allows meaningful comparison of accident statistics from one year to the next even though more or fewer workers may be present in the workplace.

Example

A large factory has 20 lost-time accidents in one year but 35 lost-time accidents the next. This appears to represent an increase of 75%, indicating that the factory's safety standards have slipped and it has become a more dangerous place to work.

However, when the number of workers employed in the factory is taken into account and the AIR for each year is calculated:

Year 1: 800 workers:

$$\text{AIR} = \frac{20}{800} \times 1{,}000 = \textbf{25 lost-time accidents per 1,000 workers}$$

Year 2: 1,500 workers:

$$\text{AIR} = \frac{35}{1{,}500} \times 1{,}000 = \textbf{23 lost-time accidents per 1,000 workers}$$

The accident rate for both years is actually very similar, so the original conclusion was incorrect. The workplace has not become more dangerous; the increase in the number of accidents occurred because more people now work in the factory.

Of course, statistics do sometimes show a false picture of what is happening in the workplace and there are times when they can be deliberately manipulated to present a desired result. Statistics should always be used and interpreted carefully to ensure that what the data seems to be showing is what is actually happening.

For example, often after a training course on accident reporting has been delivered to staff, the accident rate increases dramatically. This seems to indicate that more accidents are occurring. In fact, the same number of accidents are happening as have always happened, but now all the accidents are being reported, recorded and seen by management. The increase is caused by improved reporting, which in turn has been caused by better awareness of the reporting procedures created by the training course.

STUDY QUESTIONS

1. Define reactive and active monitoring.
2. What do we mean by systematic monitoring?
3. State the sources of information that might be used in reactive monitoring.
4. State the purpose of workplace inspections.
5. What is the difference between a safety inspection and safety tour?
6. What role does senior management have in workplace inspections?
7. Why are checklists used in inspections?
8. What should the introductory part of an inspection report contain?

(Suggested Answers are at the end.)

Investigating Incidents

IN THIS SECTION...

- Incidents should be investigated for several reasons, perhaps the most important of which is to discover the causes so that corrective action can be taken to prevent similar incidents from happening again.
- Incidents can be categorised in terms of their outcome: near miss, accident (both injury and/or damage), dangerous occurrence and ill health.
- Basic incident investigation procedure is to:
  - Gather factual information about the event.
  - Analyse that information to draw conclusions about the immediate and root causes.
  - Identify suitable control measures and then plan remedial actions.

Introduction

Unfortunately, in spite of an organisation's best efforts, accidents do happen. When they happen, it is important that the incident is reported, recorded and investigated in an appropriate and timely manner.

Function of Investigations

When an accident, or some other type of incident, occurs in the workplace it should be investigated and the investigation recorded.

There are many reasons for conducting investigations, but one of the most important is that having happened once, an accident may happen again; and when it happens again the outcome may be as bad as, or worse than, it was the first time. It is therefore important to understand exactly why the accident occurred so that corrective action can be taken to prevent a recurrence.

A workplace accident

We will look at this point in more detail when we cover the accident triangle later in this section : near misses are an indicator of accident potential. Often, the only thing that separates a near miss from an accident is luck (or chance). Where one worker trips and stumbles on the steps one day, another worker will trip, fall and break their arm the next. It follows that all incidents should be examined to determine the potential for serious harm, injury or loss. Where this potential exists, a thorough investigation should be carried out to prevent that potential from becoming actual.

This is not to say that all incidents should be thoroughly investigated in great depth and detail. That would be a waste of time and effort in many cases; but it is to say that all incidents should be examined for potential so that a decision can be made as to whether a more detailed and thorough investigation is required. This idea is sometimes formalised into an organisation's investigation procedures.

TOPIC FOCUS

Reasons for carrying out an incident investigation:

- **To identify the immediate and root causes** – incidents are usually caused by unsafe acts and unsafe conditions in the workplace, but these often arise from underlying or root causes.
- **To identify corrective action to prevent a recurrence** – a key motivation behind incident investigations.
- **To record the facts of the incident** – people do not have perfect memories and accident investigation records document factual evidence for the future.
- **For legal reasons** – accident investigations are an implicit legal duty imposed on the employer.
- **For claim management** – if a claim for compensation is lodged against the employer the insurance company will examine the accident investigation report to help determine liability.
- **For staff morale** – non-investigation of accidents has a detrimental effect on morale and safety culture because workers will assume that the organisation does not value their safety.
- **For disciplinary purposes** – though blaming workers for incidents has a negative effect on safety culture (see Element 3), there are occasions when an organisation has to discipline a worker because their behaviour has fallen short of the acceptable standard.
- **For data-gathering purposes** – accident statistics can be used to identify trends and patterns; this relies on the collection of good quality data.

Types of Incident

Incidents can be categorised according to their nature and outcome:

Accident

For example, a worker on the ground is struck on the head and killed by a brick dropped by another worker on a 5m-high scaffold; or a lorry driver misjudges the turning circle of his vehicle and knocks over a barrier at the edge of a site entrance, crushing the barrier beyond repair. Note that in both of these examples the acts are not carried out deliberately. An accident is unplanned. Any **deliberate** attempt to cause injury or loss is therefore not an accident.

DEFINITION 

ACCIDENT

An unplanned, unwanted event which leads to injury, damage or loss.

Accidents can be further subdivided into:

- **Injury accident** – an unplanned, unwanted event which leads to personal injury of some sort.
- **Damage-only accident** – an unplanned, unwanted event which leads to damage to equipment or property.

A construction worker suffers an accident

Near Miss

For example, a worker drops a brick from a 5m-high scaffold and it narrowly misses another worker standing on the ground. No injury results and the brick is not even broken. The only thing that separates accidents and near misses is the **outcome** of the event. An accident causes loss, a near miss does not.

DEFINITION 

NEAR MISS

An unplanned, unwanted event that had the potential to lead to injury, damage or loss, but did not, in fact, do so.

Dangerous Occurrence

Under the **Reporting of Injuries, Diseases and Dangerous Occurrences Regulations 2013 (RIDDOR)** certain types of event have to be reported to the relevant authority, even though no injury or ill health may have resulted. For example, the failure of the load-bearing parts of a crane is a dangerous occurrence. No person has to be injured by the failure, the failure itself is reportable. This topic is dealt with in more detail later in this element.

DEFINITION 

DANGEROUS OCCURENCE

A specified event that has to be reported to the relevant authority by statute law.

Work-Related Ill Health

For example, dermatitis is a disease of the skin often caused by work activities, especially when the handling of solvents, detergents or irritant substances is involved. Work-related ill health includes diseases and conditions related to exposure to:

- Toxic substances, e.g. lead poisoning.
- Harmful biological agents, e.g. legionnaires' disease.
- Physical or ergonomic hazards, e.g. noise-induced hearing loss.

Note that work-related ill health can refer to psychological illness, e.g. clinical depression caused by stress.

Ill health can result from a single incident. For example, it is possible to develop dermatitis as a result of a single exposure to an irritant substance. However, many forms of ill health do not result from a single incident but from ongoing or long-lasting working conditions or multiple exposures.

DEFINITION 

WORK-RELATED ILL HEALTH

Diseases or medical conditions caused by a person's work.

Psychological ill health - caused by stress at work

Accident Ratios

Accident ratios (often referred to as accident triangles) display the relationship between numbers of accidents with different outcomes. Research shows that this relationship forms a triangle, with the most serious outcomes being the least numerous (at the top) and those with proportionally higher numbers but less serious results forming the base. There are a number of different triangles used to display these relationships; one proposed by Bird is given in the following figure.

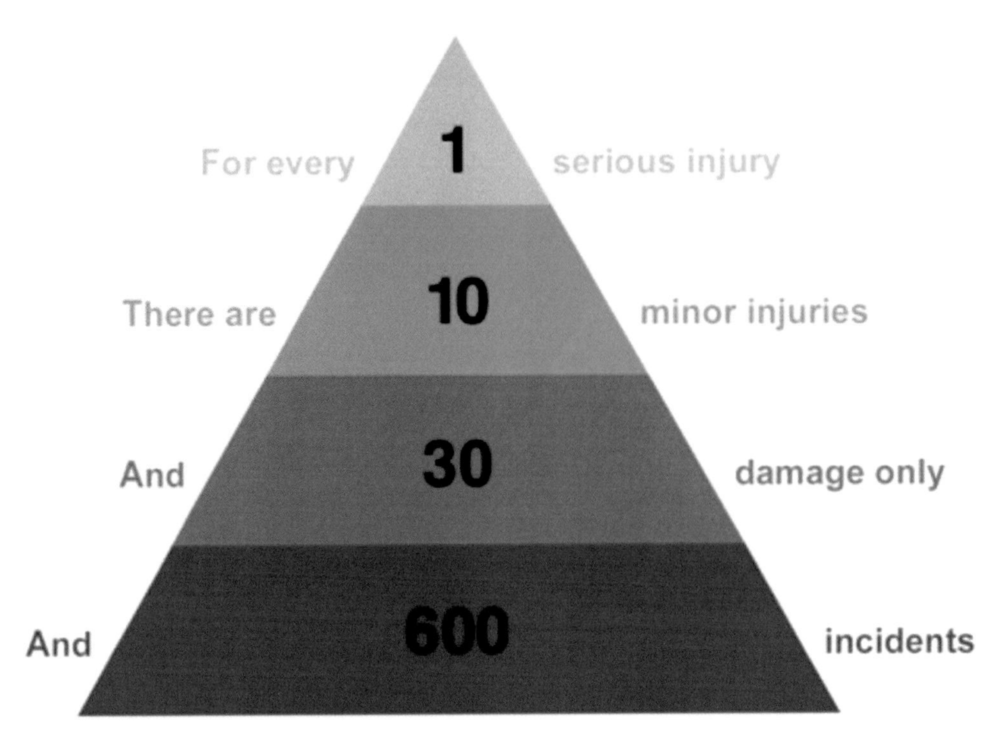

Frank Bird's Accident Triangle

The important message of the accident triangle is that serious outcome accidents tend to happen rarely and randomly. They are notoriously difficult to predict (if they were not, it would be easy to prevent them from happening). Near misses/incidents, on the other hand, happen far more frequently (600 times more frequently according to Bird). Many near misses will be minor events of little or no consequence, if they happen again there would be no serious outcome.

But some near misses will have the potential for very serious injury. These near misses should be thoroughly investigated and preventive measures put in place. In this way, a serious outcome incident is prevented.

Note that accident ratio studies are based on statistical ratios. They cannot be used to predict exactly when a certain type of event might occur. For example, just because an organisation has had 600 near misses/incidents reported does not mean that the very next type of event will be a serious injury accident. That is an over-simplification of the accident triangle. The triangle also doesn't say that every near miss could actually result in a serious injury – it is a statistical relationship only.

Basic Investigation Procedures

When investigating an accident or other types of incident, there are some basic principles and procedures that can be used:

- Step 1: Gather factual information about the event.
- Step 2: Analyse that information and draw conclusions about the immediate and root causes.
- Step 3: Identify suitable control measures.
- Step 4: Plan the remedial actions.

However, before the investigation can begin, there are two important issues that should be considered:

- **Safety of the scene** – is the area safe to approach? Is immediate action needed to eliminate danger even before casualties are approached?
- **Casualty care** – any injured people will require first-aid treatment and may need hospitalisation. This is, of course, a priority. It is also worth considering the welfare of uninjured bystanders who may be in shock.

Once immediate danger has been eliminated and casualties have been attended to, a decision may have to be made about the type or level of investigation. Is this to be a:

- Relatively simple investigation of an incident that caused no or minor outcomes and did not have the potential to cause serious outcomes?
- More in-depth and thorough investigation of an incident with serious outcomes or potential for serious outcomes?

The first type of investigation might be carried out by the line manager of the area; the second type often involves a team of investigators that might include a safety specialist, senior managers, a technical specialist and perhaps worker representatives.

Checklists can be useful tools to aid an investigation to ensure that the relevant points have been covered.

TOPIC FOCUS

Items that could be included on an accident investigation checklist could include:

- Personal details of the person involved.
- Time and location of the accident.
- Type and severity of the injury sustained.
- Whether the injured person had been given first aid, had returned to work or had been sent to hospital.
- Underlying medical condition of the injured person.
- Task being undertaken at the time of the accident.
- Working environment as far as weather, standard of lighting and visibility were concerned.
- Condition of the floor or ground.
- The type and condition of any personal protective equipment that was being worn.
- Details of the training and information received.
- Details of any relevant risk assessments that had been carried out.
- Any previous similar accidents that had occurred.

Step 1: Gathering Information

- Secure the scene as soon as possible to prevent it being altered.
- Collect witnesses' details quickly, before they start to move away. In some cases, it may help to remove witnesses from the scene and ask them to wait in a separate area. If there are many witnesses, it may be better to separate them from each other to prevent collusion or contamination of their testimony.
- Collect factual information from the scene and record it. This might be done by means of:
  - Photographs.
  - Sketches.
  - Measurements.
  - Videos.
  - Written descriptions of factors, such as wind speed, temperature, etc.
  - Taking physical evidence such as samples, or the equipment that has failed.

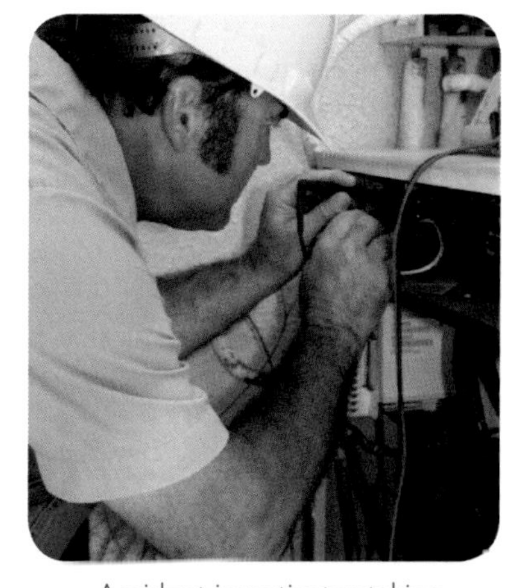

Accident investigator taking measurements

The investigator should come prepared with the appropriate equipment to record this information.

- Once the scene has been thoroughly examined, move on to the second source of information: witnesses.

  Witnesses often provide crucial evidence about what occurred before, during and after incidents. They should be interviewed carefully to make sure that good-quality evidence is gathered.

TOPIC FOCUS

Good witness interview technique requires that the interviewer should:

- Hold the interview in a quiet room or area free from distractions and interruptions.
- Introduce themselves and try to establish rapport with the witness using appropriate verbal and body language.
- Explain the purpose of the interview (perhaps emphasising that the interview is not about blaming people).
- Use open questions, such as those beginning with What?, Why?, Where?, When?, Who?, How?, etc. that do not put words into the witnesses' mouths and do not allow them to answer with a "yes" or "no".
- Keep an open mind.
- Take notes so that the facts being discussed are not forgotten.
- Ask the witness to write and sign a statement to create a record of their testimony.
- Thank the witness for their help.

- Once witnesses have been interviewed, move on to the third source of information: documentation.

  Various documents may be examined during an accident investigation, such as:

  - Company policy.
  - Risk assessments.
  - Training records.
  - Safe systems of work.
  - Permits-to-work.
  - Maintenance records.
  - Previous accident reports.
  - Sickness and absence records.

Step 2: Analysing Information

The purpose here is to draw conclusions about the **immediate** and **root** causes of the incident.

Immediate causes are the obvious causes that gave rise to the event itself. These will be the things that occurred at the time and place of the accident. For example, a worker slips on a patch of oil spilt on the floor, injuring his back as he falls backwards and hits the ground. The immediate cause of the back injury is hitting the ground, but there are many contributors to this cause. It is common to think of these in terms of unsafe acts and unsafe conditions. So here, for example, we might have the slippery oil (unsafe condition), and the worker walking through it (unsafe act).

Root causes might include:

- Failure to adequately supervise workers.
- Failure to provide appropriate PPE.
- Failure to provide adequate training.
- Lack of maintenance.

- Inadequate checking or inspections.
- Failure to carry out proper risk assessments.

For example, with the slip we described above, the root causes might be a poorly maintained machine that has leaked oil onto the floor, and a poorly inspected and maintained workshop with broken light fittings and inadequate lighting levels. Here, the worker might be blameless on the basis that, given those conditions, the accident was bound to happen eventually.

Many of the accidents that happen in workplaces have one immediate cause and one underlying or root cause. The root cause gives rise to the immediate cause which in turn gives rise to the accident (rather like a row of dominoes falling; in fact this idea is often referred to as the domino theory of accident causation).

If that one root cause is identified and dealt with then the accident should not happen again. For example, if a worker twists their ankle in a pothole in the pavement then the obvious solution is to fill the pothole in. That deals with the immediate cause. It would also be worth asking how long the pothole had been there for. If it had been there for a long time, why was it not spotted sooner? And if it had been spotted, why had it been left unrepaired with no interim measure being taken to protect people?

These questions might identify an underlying cause, such as inadequate inspection and maintenance or failure to put interim measures in place whilst waiting for maintenance work to be carried out. These root causes need to be addressed if similar accidents are to be prevented in future.

In contrast to this single cause idea, some workplace accidents are complex and have multiple causes: there are several immediate causes for the accident and each of these has one or more underlying or root cause. This idea is usually referred to as multi-causation theory. For example, a worker might be struck by a load being carried by a forklift truck.

Immediate causes for such an accident might be:

- Failure to secure the load on the pallet.
- Poor road positioning of the truck close to a pedestrian exit.
- Aggressive braking by the truck driver.
- An inattentive pedestrian stepping out in front of the truck.

On investigation each of these immediate causes might have their own separate **root causes**, such as:

- No training for the driver, who is new to the workplace, has not worked with this type of load before and is unaware of the load-securing technique required.
- Lack of segregation of pedestrian and traffic routes; no barriers and no marking to separate the two.
- Lack of proper driver induction into their new workplace so they are unaware of the layout and position of pedestrian exits, etc.
- Poor maintenance of the truck.
- No refresher training for existing staff, meaning that experienced staff have become complacent.

If there are multiple causes for the accident then it is important that each of these causes is identified during the investigation, otherwise incomplete remedial action will be taken and similar accidents may happen in the future.

Step 3: Identify Suitable Control Measures

Once the immediate and underlying causes of the accident are known, appropriate control measures can be identified. It is important that the correct control measures are established, otherwise time, money and effort will be wasted on inadequate and unnecessary measures that will not prevent similar occurrences in the future.

Control measures must be identified to remedy both the immediate and underlying causes. Immediate causes are usually easy to identify - if there is a spill of oil on the floor, clean it up; if the guard is missing from the machine, reattach it.

Underlying causes can be harder to determine because they reflect failure of the management system. But it is essential that the correct control measures to remedy the failure of the management system are identified, because this will help prevent similar accidents occurring in similar circumstances across the entire organisation. For example, if a worker slips on some oil that has leaked out of a vehicle in the distribution depot, an employer may:

- Clean up the oil leaking out of the vehicle (the immediate cause), but fail to deal with the underlying cause (lack of inspection and maintenance). This could lead to more leaks, which in turn would lead to more pedestrian slips (and perhaps, vehicle skids).
- Clean up the oil leaking out of the vehicle and deal with the underlying cause (by introducing a proper inspection and maintenance system). In this instance, there is a good chance that most oil leaks will be prevented in the future for all vehicles in the fleet at all locations.

Perhaps the most important questions to ask when identifying control measures are:

- If this action is taken, will it prevent this same accident from happening in exactly the same way at this location?
- If this action is taken, will it prevent other similar types of accident from happening in similar locations in the future?

If the answer to both of these questions is "no", then you need to identify other control measures.

Step 4: Plan the Remedial Actions

An accident investigation should lead to corrective action being taken, in just the same way as a workplace inspection will. Remedial actions can be presented in an action plan:

Recommended action	Priority	Timescale	Responsible person
Introduce induction training for all new drivers	Medium	1 month	Warehouse manager

When the action plan is being prepared, appropriate immediate and interim control measures must be given suitable priorities and timescales. Unsafe conditions must not be allowed to persist in the workplace. Dangerous practices and high-risk activities must be dealt with immediately. This means that immediate action must be taken to remedy these circumstances when they are discovered. Machinery and equipment may have to be taken out of action, certain work activities suspended, and locations evacuated. These responses cannot be left until the investigation has been completed. They will have to be implemented immediately to ensure safety while the investigation is in progress.

STUDY QUESTIONS

9. What is the prime purpose of an accident investigation?
10. What are the four elements of the investigation process?
11. Identify the categories of staff who might be considered useful members of an internal accident investigation team.
12. List the types of documentation which might be consulted during an accident investigation.
13. What are the two categories of immediate cause of accidents/incidents?
14. An employee has been hit by a reversing vehicle in a loading bay. List possible immediate causes and root causes.

(Suggested Answers are at the end.)

Recording and Reporting Incidents

IN THIS SECTION...

- Arrangements should be made for the internal reporting of all work-related incidents and workers should be encouraged to report.
- Records of work-related injuries must be kept. There is a standard accident book that can be used for this purpose.
- Certain types of incident have to be reported to the enforcing authorities in a specific way to a timescale to comply with statutory requirements (**Reporting of Injuries, Diseases and Dangerous Occurrences Regulations 2013 (RIDDOR)**).
- These 'reportable' incidents include fatalities, specified injuries, dangerous occurrences, occupational diseases, over-seven-day injuries, flammable gas incidents and dangerous gas fittings.
- Data collected from incident reports can be used for statistical analysis to identify patterns and trends in the workplace.
- Incident statistics can be used to communicate safety performance to various groups within the organisation, such as the safety committee, senior management and the workforce.

Recording and Reporting Requirements

Work-related incidents, including near misses, should be reported internally by workers to management. The system put in place by an organisation to allow for this should be described in the **Arrangements** section of the organisation's safety policy.

It is standard practice for workers to report incidents to their immediate line manager verbally, followed by completion of an internal incident report form that records the incident.

There are occasions when this simple verbal reporting procedure is not appropriate and a more complex reporting procedure then has to be introduced. For example, a lone-working contractor visiting a client's premises may have to report their accident to the client as well as to their remote line manager.

DEFINITION 

REPORTING

The process of informing people that an incident has occurred – this can be internally within the organisation or externally to enforcing authorities or insurers, etc.

RECORDING

The process of documenting the event

Internal Incident Reporting

When establishing an incident-reporting policy, the organisation should be clear about the type of incident that has to be reported by workers. It is usual to include a list of definitions in the policy so that workers understand the phrases used. If the organisation wants workers to report near misses it must specify this in the policy and be clear about what that phrase actually means.

Having established an incident-reporting policy, the organisation must encourage workers to report all relevant incidents. Unfortunately, there are many reasons why workers do not report incidents.

TOPIC FOCUS

Reasons why workers might not report accidents:

- Unclear organisational policy.
- No reporting system in place.
- Overly-complicated reporting procedures.
- Excessive paperwork.
- Takes too much time.
- Blame culture.
- Apathy.
- Lack of training on policy and procedures.

The organisation should try to remove each of these barriers to ensure that every relevant incident is reported in a timely manner. Most of these barriers can be dealt with by having a well-prepared, clearly stated policy, adopting user-friendly procedures and paperwork, and training staff in the procedures. An organisation can take disciplinary action against workers who fail to report incidents if they have been given the training and means to do so.

Sometimes it is not sufficient simply to report an incident to immediate line management, sometimes a higher-profile response is necessary. When fatal or major injuries, high-cost dangerous occurrences, high-profile incidents or environmental events occur, it will be necessary to notify certain internal personnel immediately. Directors, senior managers, human resources managers, health and safety and/or environmental managers and worker representatives may all have to be notified. Action by these staff may then be required to inform external parties as necessary, e.g. the family of the casualty, external authorities, insurance companies, public relations advisers, etc. These internal and external contact procedures are often documented in the incident-reporting section of an organisation's safety policy.

Incident Recording and the Accident Book

When a work-related incident is reported, a record is usually created of that event (in some instances the report is filed in written form, so reporting and recording are one and the same thing).

As a minimum, organisations must keep a record of all work-related accidents that result in personal injury.

This is dictated by social security legislation and there is a standard accident book that can be used. The accident book provides a record on any injury (or disease) which could give rise to a claim for Industrial Injuries Disablement Benefit. Without such a record, the benefits can be harder to obtain.

This accident book contains a form that is completed to make a record of each accident. This record must then be removed from the book and kept by a responsible person under lock and key in order to comply with the **Data Protection Act 1998** (which seeks to ensure that personal information is only kept and used for legitimate purposes and that access to that personal information is restricted to those with a legitimate need). These records have to be kept for a minimum of three years.

There is no fixed format for an accident report form. Organisations can use any format, as long as certain standard information is recorded

Organisations do not have to use the standard accident book. They can design their own in-house forms, which is often better to take account of near misses and other incidents that may not be covered on the standard form. But these forms must contain the basic information that is collected by the standard accident book as a minimum if they include accident reporting.

TOPIC FOCUS

Typical contents of an accident record:

- Name and address of casualty.
- Date and time of accident.
- Location of accident.
- Details of injury.
- Details of treatment given.
- Description of event causing injury.
- Details of any equipment or substances involved.
- Witnesses' names and contact details.
- Details of person completing the record.
- Signatures.

Organisations often have separate forms for the recording of accidents (as above) and the recording of accident investigations. Separate forms can also take account of near misses (see below). These do not need to record standard accident book data.

TOPIC FOCUS

Typical contents of a near-miss report form:

- Name of person making the report.
- Date and time of near miss.
- Location of the near miss.
- Details of the near miss.
- Description of event(s) causing near miss.
- Details of any loss or damage caused.
- Immediate causes.
- Root causes.
- Actions to prevent recurrence.

The Reporting of Injuries, Diseases and Dangerous Occurrences Regulations 2013 (RIDDOR)

The **Reporting of Injuries, Diseases and Dangerous Occurrences Regulations 2013 (RIDDOR)** require the reporting of certain types of event (reportable events) to the relevant enforcing authorities.

A nominated responsible person should be identified by the employer for carrying out **RIDDOR** reporting requirements. This would usually be done in the arrangements section of the health and safety policy.

There are five main types of reportable event:

- **Fatality** – where any person dies as a result of a work-related injury.

- **Specified injuries** – where a worker suffers one of the specified injuries shown in Schedule 1 to the Regulations (see examples below).
- **Dangerous occurrences** – where one of the 'near-miss' type occurrences happens, shown in Schedule 2.
- **Work-related illness** – where a worker suffers one of the eight categories of reportable work-related illnesses.
- **Over-seven-day injuries** – where a worker suffers an injury that prevents them doing their normal work for more than seven days.

Specified injuries include:

- A fracture, other than to fingers, thumbs and toes.
- Amputation of an arm, hand, finger, thumb, leg, foot or toe.
- Permanent loss of sight or reduction of sight.
- Crush injuries leading to internal organ damage.
- Serious burns (covering more than 10% of the body, or causing damage to the eyes, respiratory system or other vital organs).
- Scalpings (separation of the skin from the head) which require hospital treatment.
- Unconsciousness caused by head injury or asphyxia.
- Any other injury arising from working in an enclosed space, which leads to hypothermia, heat-induced illness or requires resuscitation or admittance to hospital for more than 24 hours.

Over-seven-day injuries to workers are where an employee or self-employed person is away from work or unable to perform their normal work duties for more than seven consecutive days (not counting the day of the accident).

Injuries to non-workers may be reportable where work-related injuries involve members of the public or people who are not at work. They only need reporting where a person is injured and taken from the scene of the accident to hospital **for treatment** to that injury. The key phrase here is "for treatment" - diagnostic tests like x-rays don't constitute treatment.

Reportable occupational diseases include the diagnosis (by a medical practitioner) of:

- Carpal tunnel syndrome.
- Severe cramp of the hand or forearm.
- Occupational dermatitis.
- Hand-arm vibration syndrome.
- Occupational asthma.
- Tendonitis or tenosynovitis of the hand or forearm.
- An occupational cancer.
- Any disease attributed to an occupational exposure to a biological agent.

A **dangerous occurrence** is itself reportable and does not have to have caused a reportable injury. The 27 categories of dangerous occurrence include:

- The collapse, overturning or failure of load-bearing parts of lifts and lifting equipment.
- Plant or equipment coming into contact with overhead power lines.
- Explosions or fires causing work to be stopped for more than 24 hours.

Reportable gas incidents concern distributors and supplies, etc. of flammable gas, and Gas Safe registered engineers. Certain listed events causing or having the potential to cause death or injury are to be reported.

Once one of these reportable events has occurred, it must be reported to the HSE.

Reporting

- Most incidents, including fatalities, specified injuries and dangerous occurrences must be notified by 'quickest practicable means' without delay. This can be done using an online notification report form.
- Fatalities and specified injuries can be reported by telephone to the HSE Incident Contact Centre.
- For all of the above incidents, an online report must be submitted within 10 days of the incident occurring.
- **Over-seven-day injuries** must be reported using the online report form within 15 days of the injury occurring. There is no requirement for immediate notification.
- **Reportable diseases** must be reported using the online report upon written confirmation of diagnosis by a medical practitioner.
- **All reportable events** are to be reported online, using the appropriate F2508 form (of which there are various versions).

Type of Event	Immediate Notification Required	Written Report Timescale
Fatality	Yes	10 days
Specified injury	Yes	10 days
Dangerous occurence	Yes	10 days
Over-7-day injury*	No	15 days
Reportable disease	No	'forthwith' After diagnosis by a doctor
*Over-seven-day injuries must be notified within 15 days of the incident. Over-3-day injuries are **recordable** but not reportable.		

Record-Keeping

Records of **RIDDOR** reportable events must be kept by the responsible person for a minimum of three years. This is usually done by printing out and keeping a copy of the online **RIDDOR** report form.

RIDDOR also requires that a record of all 'over-three-day injuries' is kept for a minimum of three years.

An 'over-three-day injury' is a work-related accident that causes an injury that results in a worker being away from work or incapacitated for more than three consecutive days (not counting the day of the accident but including any weekends or other rest days). Over-three-day injuries **do not** have to be reported to the authorities unless the incapacitation period goes on to exceed seven days. Normally the standard injury report form that must be kept for all work-related injuries is sufficient to meet the over-three-day injury recording requirement.

Form F2508IE Report of an Injury follows. Make a note of the main headings and the basic information that has to be submitted.

Health and Safety Executive

Close window

Report of an injury

Note: this is a preview of your form and does NOT represent the submitted details of your notification, which will include the Notification number for reference

About you and your organisation

Notifier name			
Job title			
Organisation name			
Address			
Phone no		Fax Number	
Email Address			

Where did the incident happen

About the incident

Incident Date		Incident Time	
In which local authority did the incident occur (Country, Geographical Area and Local Authority)?			
..			
In which department or where on the premises did the incident happen?			
What type of work was being carried out (generally the main business activity of the site)?			
--			

About the kind of accident

Kind of accident	
Work process involved	
Main factor involved	
What happened	

About the injured person

Injured persons name			
Injured persons address			
Phone no		What was their occupation or job title?	
Gender		Age	
Work Status			

About the injured person's injuries

Severity of the injury			
Injuries		Part of the body affected	

F2508IE Report of an Injury

Source: HSE (https://extranet.hse.gov.uk/lfserver/external/F2508IE)

Internal Data Collection, Analysis and Communication

Once an incident has been reported and a record has been made, that record should be collected by a nominated responsible person. Information can then be extracted from the report and the report filed.

Any accident report, **RIDDOR** report and accident investigation report relating to an accident that has taken place at work should be carefully filed for future reference. Not only is it a legal duty to keep accident reports and **RIDDOR** reports for three years, but these records may be examined in the event of a civil claim for compensation made by the injured person. These reports form an important written record of events and they carry some weight since they are created at the time of the accident rather than being based on recollections made some time after. They can be important sources of information for the insurance companies, solicitors and barristers involved.

When information is extracted from accident report forms, the data might then be entered into a computer database for analysis. In this way, useful information about trends and patterns can be obtained. This can be done using standard spreadsheet applications or custom-designed software.

The exact nature of the analysis will depend on the information that was collected on the incident report in the first place. Analysis might be able to answer questions, such as:

- What is the trend in accident incidence rate over the last five years?
- What are the most common types of accident?
- What are the most common types of injury?
- Between what times of day do most accidents occur?
- Which part of the body is most frequently injured?
- Which department has the highest accident rate?
- What is the accident rate trend for a particular part of the organisation?
- Where do most accidents occur in the workplace?

This information can then be used to target certain areas of performance where problems have been identified.

For example, if an increase in the number of hand injuries in a particular department has been highlighted, this can be investigated. If there has been an overall decrease in the accident rate over the last five years, but that trend has reversed over the last year, research can be carried out into the reasons for this.

Within an organisation there are certain people who may be interested in this incident data and its interpretation:

- Directors – who have to report on safety performance to shareholders.
- Senior management – responsible for developing policy and allocating resources.
- The health and safety committee – involved in steering the organisational strategy.
- Worker representatives – concerned about protecting the interests of workers.
- Workers themselves.

Different types of report might be prepared for different target audiences. It is customary to post information about accident statistics on notice boards.

MORE... www.

www.hse.gov.uk/riddor/report.htm

STUDY QUESTIONS

15. Who is usually responsible for initially reporting accidents and other safety-related incidents?
16. What is the purpose of analysing information about accidents?
17. To whom do the results of accident investigations have to be communicated?
18. What are the five main categories of reportable incidents under **RIDDOR**?
19. Which events have to be reported straightaway under **RIDDOR**, and how?
20. For how long should records of reportable incidents be kept?
21. Which occupational diseases must be reported?
22. Apart from the accident documentation about the particular incident, what other information may be relevant to a claim for damages in respect of injuries suffered as a result of a guard malfunctioning on a drill?
23. What actions should be taken following a serious injury at work?

(Suggested Answers are at the end.)

Summary

This element has dealt with active and reactive monitoring, investigating incidents and recording and reporting incidents.

In particular, this element has:

- Differentiated between active monitoring (checking to ensure that standards are met before any untoward event takes place) and reactive monitoring (measuring safety performance by reference to accidents, incidents and ill health that have already occurred).
- Outlined some active monitoring methods (inspections, sampling, tours and surveys) and explained the factors that must be considered when setting up an inspection system.
- Considered how to write an effective inspection report.
- Outlined how data collected from incident reports can be used for statistical analysis to identify patterns and trends in the workplace.
- Considered the reasons for accident investigation, perhaps the most important of which is to discover the causes so that corrective action can be taken to prevent similar accidents from happening again.
- Categorised incidents in terms of their outcome: near miss, accident (both injury and/or damage), dangerous occurrence and ill health.
- Described a basic investigation procedure:
  - Gather factual information about the event.
  - Analyse that information to draw conclusions about the immediate and root causes.
  - Identify suitable control measures.
  - Plan remedial actions.
- Outlined the arrangements that should be made for the internal reporting of all work-related incidents and the records of work-related injuries that should be kept.
- Described the requirements of **RIDDOR** and the types of incident that have to be reported to the enforcing authorities, such as fatalities, specified injuries, dangerous occurrences, occupational diseases and over-seven-day injuries.

Exam Skills

QUESTION

Outline how the following may be used to improve safety performance within an organisation:

(a) accident data; (5)

(b) safety inspections. (3)

Approaching the Question

Now think about the steps you would take to answer this question:

Step 1: The first step is to read the question carefully. Note that this question asks you to outline how accident data and safety inspections can be used to improve safety performance. So for an outline you need to give the most important features of accident data and safety inspections.

Step 2: Next, consider the marks available. In this question there are eight marks, so it is expected that around eight or nine different pieces of information should be provided. Questions that are split into parts (this one is split into two parts worth five and three marks respectively) are often easier to pick up marks on, because the signposts NEBOSH use are so much easier to see. In the first part, the question asks for an outline of how accident data may be used to improve safety performance and is worth five marks, so you will need five or six points in this part. The second part is on safety inspections and worth three marks, so three or four points will be sufficient. The question should take around eight minutes in total.

Step 3: Now highlight the key words. In this case, they might look like this:

Outline how the following may be used to improve safety performance within an organisation:

(a) accident data; (5)

(b) safety inspections. (3)

Step 4: Read the question again to make sure you understand it and have a clear understanding of how you can improve safety performance using accident data and safety inspections. (Re-read your notes if you need to.)

Step 5: The next stage is to develop a plan – there are various ways to do this. Remind yourself, first of all, that you need to be thinking about 'improvements to safety performance' - for the first part, how accident statistics can improve performance, and for the second part, how safety inspections can improve performance. When you see the action word 'Outline', you need to give the most important features of the terms. So, the answer plan will take the form of a bullet-pointed list that you need to develop into a full answer.

Your answer must be based on the key words you have highlighted. So, in this case we need to outline how we can improve safety performance using accident statistics and safety inspections.

Suggested Answer

Plan

Accident Data
• Identify trends and problem areas. • Allocation of resources. • Benchmarking. • Show the cost of accidents. • Focus minds and discussion.
Safety Inspections
• Demonstrate management commitment. • Involve employees and safety representatives. • Prompt actions to safety concerns improve morale. • Check conformance to standards. • Identify problems before an accident happens.

Example of How the Question Could be Answered

(a) *Accident data may be used to improve an organisation's safety performance by identifying accident trends, (e.g. slips and trips) in specific areas, (e.g. kitchens) and to enable management to focus resources on these specific aspects to reduce the recurrence rate. The organisation may use accident data to compare itself with a similar organisation (benchmarking) to establish whether it should be doing more to improve safety, or to establish whether the cost of not managing safety is reducing the organisation's market competitiveness. Accident data can be used to calculate the cost of not managing safety to ensure business cases for safety initiatives can succeed on a cost/benefit basis. Accident data can be discussed at safety committees or provided as information to employees to stimulate discussion at team briefings or meetings and to engage employees in safety improvements.*

(b) *Safety inspections carried out by management can be used to improve safety performance by demonstrating top-level commitment. Safety inspections can also be used positively to involve the employees by inviting them to take part in the inspection (to see failings at first hand) or by holding meetings to discuss the findings from safety inspections, increasing worker ownership in safety. Safety inspections will identify conformance to standards, giving management an opportunity to rectify non-conformance before an accident happens.*

Reasons for Poor Marks Achieved by Candidates in Exam

- Wasting time by concentrating on reasons for collecting accident data and not saying how it can be used to improve business performance.
- Describing how a safety inspection should be conducted, who should take part and frequency – this is not the question set and will gain no marks.

Element 5

Act

Learning Outcomes

Once you've read this element, you'll understand how to:

1. Explain the purpose of, and procedures for, health and safety auditing.
2. Explain the purpose of, and procedures for, regular reviews of health and safety performance.

Contents

Auditing

IN THIS SECTION...

- Auditing is the systematic, objective, critical evaluation of an organisation's health and safety management system.
- Preparations have to be made prior to an audit commencing.
- During an audit, three different types of evidence will be sought: documents and records, interviews, and direct observation in the workplace.
- Audit reports feed information back into the review process so that action can be taken for continual improvement.
- Audits can be conducted by external personnel and by internal staff. There are strengths and weaknesses to both types.

Definition, Scope and Purpose of Auditing

Auditing can be defined as:

> *"The structured process of collecting independent information on the efficiency, effectiveness and reliability of the total health and safety management system and drawing up plans for corrective action".*

TOPIC FOCUS

A shorter definition might be that auditing is the "systematic, objective, critical evaluation of how well an organisation's management system is performing by examining evidence".

Health and safety audits share many common features with financial, quality and environmental management audits; the basic principles are the same.

Auditing is a mechanism for verifying that an organisation's safety management system is in place and operating effectively.

The intention of an audit is to provide critical feedback on the management system so that appropriate follow-up action can be taken. An audit can, therefore, be viewed as negative since it will tend to focus on areas of weakness and non-conformance. In fact, some audits do not make any mention of any positive aspects of the safety management system at all; they focus entirely on the weaknesses. This is, however, inherent in the purpose of the audit – to identify weaknesses so that they can be dealt with. Auditing is another form of active monitoring.

Audit - structured process of collecting information

The Distinction Between Audits and Inspections

An **audit** focuses on management systems; it:

- Examines documents such as the safety policy, arrangements, procedures, risk assessments, safe systems of work, method statements, etc.
- Looks closely at records such as those created to verify training, maintenance, inspections, statutory examinations, etc.
- Verifies the standards that exist within the workplace by interview and direct observation.

An **inspection** is a simpler process of checking the workplace for uncontrolled hazards and addressing any that are found.

It is important that the term "audit" is used correctly – an audit is the thorough examination of the process, from the documents through to what is happening in practice in the workplace. We might "inspect" the fire extinguishers, but we can "audit" the fire precautions for the site to ensure that:

- There is a fire risk assessment and that it is suitable.
- The controls in the assessment are implemented in practice.
- The personnel are aware of them.
- The training records are in place.
- The maintenance inspections are carried out.
- The fire drills are complete, etc.

The Audit Process from Preparation to Follow-up

Different audits are run in slightly different ways. What follows is a fairly typical audit process.

Pre-Audit Preparations

Before the audit starts, the following should be defined:

- Date and time of the audit – so that all necessary resources and personnel can be made available during the audit.
- The scope of the audit – will it cover health and safety, or will other topics such as environmental management be included as well? Will it be fully comprehensive (which may take weeks) or more selective?
- The area and extent of the audit – one department? One whole site? All sites?
- Who will be required – auditors will need to be accompanied during their visit and will need access to managers for information.
- Information-gathering – it is common practice for auditors to ask for copies of relevant documentation (such as policy documents) before starting the audit so that they can prepare.

Auditor examining policy documents

The organisation will have to ensure that the auditor is competent; i.e. that they have the relevant qualifications, experience and knowledge to do the job well. This can apply to both internal and external auditors.

If internal staff are used as auditors, that will require the allocation of sufficient time and resources so that they can be trained and developed in that role.

All of these matters require the allocation of sufficient management time and resources.

During the Audit

Auditors use three methods to gather factual information:

- Reference to paperwork – the documents and records which indicate what should be happening and what has happened relevant to a particular issue.
- Interviews – word-of-mouth evidence given by managers and workers.
- Direct observation – of the workplace, equipment, activities and behaviour.

Auditors will sometimes seek to collect evidence so that their findings cannot be refuted; this can be done by copying paperwork, taking photographs and having a witness to corroborate word-of-mouth evidence.

An auditor's favourite phrases are: "Show me" and "Prove it".

TOPIC FOCUS

Typical information examined during an audit:

- Health and safety policy.
- Roles and responsibilities.
- Risk assessments and the control of any specific hazards.
- Training records.
- Contractor control records and arrangements.
- Minutes of safety committee meetings.
- Maintenance records.
- Accident investigation reports.
- Emergency arrangements such as fire prevention.
- Inspection reports.
- Enforcement history and actions arising.
- Recommendations from other audits.

At the End of the Audit

Verbal feedback is usually provided at the end of an audit; for some audits, this will involve a presentation to the management team. This verbal feedback will usually be followed by a written report. The report will make recommendations for improvement with an indication of priorities and timescales.

It is essential that an audit is followed up with action to correct non-conformities. These corrective actions will usually be checked during the next audit. In some auditing systems, this will be done through an interim follow-up visit or audit that simply looks at the way that the previous audit recommendations have been addressed.

Responsibility for Audits

It is the responsibility of the organisation to establish and implement health and safety auditing. There are circumstances when external authorities such as enforcement authorities or insurance companies will carry out audits; or an organisation may have to be audited in order to achieve or maintain certain certifications, (e.g. **OHSAS 18001** certification).

Once an audit has been carried out and feedback has been received in the form of recommendations for improvement, it is the responsibility of management to ensure that the feedback is acted upon. This is normally done through the review process (discussed later in this element) with the creation of action plans.

External and Internal Audits

Audits are often carried out by safety specialists from outside the organisation; they can also be done by in-house staff. In many instances, both types of audit are carried out at different frequencies by the organisation.

There are advantages and disadvantages to both types.

	Advantages	Disadvantages
External Audits	• Independent of any internal influence. • Fresh pair of eyes. • May have wider experience of different types of workplace. • Recommendations often carry more weight.	• Expensive. • Time consuming. • May not understand the business so make impractical suggestions. • May intimidate workers so get incomplete evidence.
Internal Audits	• Less expensive. • Auditors already know the business so know what can be realistically achieved. • Improves ownership of issues found. • Builds competence internally.	• Auditors may not notice certain issues. • Auditors may not have good knowledge of industry or legal standards. • Auditors may not possess auditing skills so may need training. • Auditors are not independent so may be subject to internal influence.

STUDY QUESTIONS

1. Define health and safety auditing.
2. Outline the differences between health and safety audits and workplace inspections.

(Suggested Answers are at the end.)

Reviewing Health and Safety Performance

IN THIS SECTION...

- Reviewing health and safety performance should be done by managers at all levels within the organisation on a routine basis to ensure that management systems are working effectively.
- Reviewing performance relies on data gathered from various sources such as accident data, inspection reports, absence data, safety tours and audits.
- Safety specialists usually play a key role in collecting this data and reporting on performance.
- Senior management then have a role in evaluating this information so that appropriate priorities and resources can be allocated.
- Reviews enable action to be taken so that health and safety performance is continually improved.

Purpose of Regular Reviews

Reviewing health and safety performance is a key part of any health and safety management system (such as the HSG65 model outlined in Element 2). Reviews should be carried out by managers at all levels within the organisation on a scheduled routine basis. Each review is likely to have a different focus and will be conducted at different intervals. For example, a review of safety management might be undertaken at the highest level of the organisation (board of directors/senior management) on an annual basis, whilst a review of local department performance might be conducted every month.

The essence of the review process is to answer the questions:

- Are we on target?
- If not, why not?
- What do we have to change?

For example, an objective for the organisation set by the board of directors was to achieve a 5% reduction in the lost-time accident incidence rate within one year. The board reviewed performance at the end of that year. A 6% reduction had been achieved:

- the answer to the first question is that the target has been met (actually exceeded),
- the second question is redundant, and
- the answer to the third question might be – set a new objective of achieving another 5% reduction next year!

Are we on target?

Records of routine performance review should be kept to demonstrate that these reviews are taking place. These records can themselves be used as a performance indicator and form a data source for the review process.

Routine performance reviews are sometimes required by a specific management standard, (e.g. **OHSAS 18001**) and, where this is the case, records of reviews may be mandatory to prove compliance with the standard.

Performance Indicators

Reviewing health and safety performance relies to a great extent on having good-quality, reliable information about current and past performance, which usually depends on data-gathering. One of the first steps in the review process is the identification of these performance indicators and then the gathering of information and data from various sources:

- **Accident and incident data** – concerning injury accidents, property damage accidents, lost-time accidents, reportable events, etc., often taken from accident records and accident investigation reports.
- **Inspections** – information and data gathered from general workplace inspection reports and statutory inspections.
- **Absence and sickness data** – concerning work-related ill health, from absence monitoring records or perhaps the occupational health department (if one exists).
- **Safety surveys, tours and sampling** – may provide evidence of conformance or non-conformance to standards.
- **Audit reports** – may present detailed and comprehensive information on the safety management system and its effectiveness.
- **Achievement of objectives** – where specific targets have been set for the organisation as a whole or parts of the organisation and achievement towards these targets has been measured.
- **Enforcement action** – such as reports from inspectors, enforcement notices and prosecutions.
- **Previous management reviews** – in particular, the completion of actions identified during those reviews.
- **Legal and best practice developments** – it is important that the organisation remains up-to-date with its legal responsibilities and responds to any changes. There may also be technological or best practice changes that can be taken into consideration to further improve the workplace.
- **Other sources** – such as:
  - Quality assurance reports.
  - Results of participation and consultation.
  - Communications and complaints from external sources.

These performance indicators can then be used to evaluate the performance of the organisation against the required standards.

These standards might be:

- Legal standards established by legislation.
- Organisational standards that go above and beyond legal compliance.

Recording Management Reviews

Records of management reviews should be retained. There may be retention durations set within standards, but in any case the reviews should be recorded in order to demonstrate that an adequate review was carried out in accordance with the **Management of Health and Safety at Work Regulations 1999**.

Reporting on Performance

It is good practice to make line managers responsible for reporting on health and safety performance for the areas under their control. This ensures that they view health and safety as one of their personal responsibilities; it creates ownership and raises the profile of health and safety. In some cases, line managers are in a position to gather information and data on health and safety performance themselves. In many instances, however, line managers will rely to some degree on the safety specialist (safety officer, manager or co-ordinator) to provide that information. The safety specialist is well placed to collect evidence about performance and will usually be responsible for reporting on safety performance to senior management/directors.

Routine performance review meeting

Role of Senior Management

The board of directors/senior management have a crucial role to play in reviewing health and safety performance across the entire organisation on a periodic basis, often annually. This review will normally rely on information collected and prepared by the safety specialist. The board/senior team may be required to make a declaration or statement to stakeholders based on this review.

As a result of the review, senior management may re-assess the policy statement and update it if required. Most importantly, they should use the review process as an opportunity to prioritise and allocate resources. What are the new priorities for the organisation in light of the review? What resources need to be provided to allow these priorities to be achieved?

Continual Improvement

The purpose of the review process at all levels of the organisation is to answer the three questions mentioned earlier (Are we on target? If not, why not? What do we have to change?). Since strategic targets are set by senior management, it makes sense for these targets to be channelled down through the organisation:

- **Senior management** set strategic targets.
- **Middle management** review performance in the areas under their control and set targets to bring their area in line with the strategic targets.
- **Junior management** review performance and set local targets that will collectively allow the strategic targets to be achieved.

This requires that health and safety reviews, at all levels, feed directly into action plans. These plans should identify the actions to be taken by responsible persons by appropriate deadlines. In this way, continual improvement of health and safety performance can be achieved.

STUDY QUESTIONS

3. What is the purpose of reviewing health and safety performance?
4. Who should take part in reviews of the occupational health and safety management system?
5. How often should reviews of the occupational health and safety management system take place?
6. What typical outputs from the management review need to be documented and maintained as a record of the review process and as evidence of its effectiveness?

(Suggested Answers are at the end.)

Summary

This element has dealt with auditing and reviewing performance.

In particular, this element has:

- Defined auditing as the systematic, objective, critical evaluation of an organisation's health and safety management system.
- Outlined the steps of an audit process, considered the types of information that might be used as evidence and identified the strengths and weaknesses of external and internal auditing.
- Outlined the part that performance review has to play in ensuring continual improvement.
- Identified the performance indicators that might be used in reporting performance and the role that senior management then have in the review process in establishing priorities and resources.

Exam Skills

QUESTION

(a) **Give** the meaning of the term 'health and safety audit'. (2)

(b) **Outline** key areas that may be covered within a health and safety audit. (10)

(c) **Explain** how the findings of a health and safety audit can be used to improve health and safety performance. (8)

Approaching the Question

Think now about the steps you would take to answer the question::

Step 1: The first step is to read the question carefully. Note that for part (a) of the question you are required to give the meaning of a term, so you need to provide, without explaining, the meaning of 'health and safety audit'. Part (b) requires an outline, so you will need to pick the most important features of a health and safety audit. Part (c) requires you to explain how the findings from an audit can be used to improve performance, so you will need to give a clear account of this process.

Step 2: Next, consider the marks available. In this question there are 20 marks available. Questions that are split into parts (this question is split into three parts worth two, ten and eight marks respectively) are often easier to pick up marks on, because the signposts NEBOSH use are so much easier to see with the question broken down into smaller sections. In part (a) of the question you are asked to 'give' the meaning of the term, which is worth two marks. So you should be able to provide this meaning in one sentence. Part (b) is worth ten marks so you need to outline at least ten factors to gain all the marks available. Part (c) is worth eight marks and since an 'explanation' of how findings can be used to improve health and safety performance will take the form of sentences, you will need between four and six sentences. The whole question should take around 25 minutes to write up and five minutes to read through and make any minor changes or additions.

Step 3: Now highlight the key words. In this case they might look like this:

Give the meaning of the term 'health and safety audit'. (2)

Outline key areas that may be covered within a health and safety audit. (10)

Explain how the findings of a health and safety audit can be used to improve health and safety performance. (8)

Step 4: Read the question again to make sure you understand it and have a clear understanding of audits. (Re-read your notes if you need to, and HSG65 "Managing for Health and Safety" if you can.)

Step 5: The next stage is to develop a plan – there are various ways to do this. First, remind yourself that this question is all about auditing, what an audit is, what an audit is, what it entails and how audits benefit the organisation. To construct your sentence for part (a), list the elements in an audit and then write them into a sentence. For part (b), again list the key factors that the audit will cover so that you can construct your outline answer by placing each factor into a sentence. Using examples to illustrate your answer will help convince the examiner that you understand the requirement for this aspect of the audit. For part (c), you will need to list how the findings can benefit the organisation - each bullet-pointed item on this list should have related subsections to give you the depth that is needed to meet the requirements for an 'explanation'. So, the answer plan will take the form of bullet pointed lists that you need to develop into a full answer.

Your answer must be based on the key words you have highlighted. So, in relation to health and safety audits we need to (a) give the meaning, (b) outline key areas and (c) explain how findings from an audit can improve performance.

Your answer must be based on the key words you have highlighted. So, in this case we need to **give** examples in each case, **outline** the purpose and legal status of a piece of legislation and an ACoP.

Suggested Answer Outline

Plan

Part (a)
• Structured. • Systematic. • Critical. • Independent. • Information. • Effectiveness. • Reliability. • Corrective actions.
Part (b)
• Health and Safety Policy. • Allocation of roles and responsibilities. • Risk assessments. • Specific hazard control. • Fire safety. • First-aid. • Contractors. • Accident reporting. • Consultation. • Maintenance of records. • Recommendations.
Part (c)
• Compliance v. non-compliance and reasons for failure. • Strengths and weaknesses, enabling benchmarking. • Informing and enabling remedial action. • Evidence of commitment to Health and Safety; communicate findings. • Prioritising and resource allocation. • Continual improvement.

When you have an answer plan that meets the requirements of the question, have a go at providing a full answer under examination conditions. Give yourself 20 minutes to write the answer (this time-frame assumes you have spent five minutes on the answer plan). Your handwriting must be legible - if the examiner cannot read what is written then it cannot be marked. You will not be penalised in the exam for poor grammar or spelling, as long as your answer is clear and can be understood.

Remember, you can always contact your tutor if you have any queries or need any further guidance on how to answer this question.

When you have finished your answer, read the suggested answer below and compare it to your answer.

Example of How the Question Could be Answered

(a) *A structured, systematic, critical review of independent information collected on the effectiveness and reliability of the organisation's health and safety management system and suggested corrective actions.*

(b) *The key areas to be covered by a health and safety audit would be the organisation's Health and Safety Policy, ensuring that one existed and that it was communicated to the employees. The audit should check that roles and responsibilities for health and safety have been allocated to individuals and that they understand their roles. The audit can review risk assessments to ensure they are suitable and sufficient, they are current and actions identified on them completed. The audit should ensure that specific hazards such as manual handling, work at height or the control of substances hazardous to health are appropriately managed. Auditors can ensure that fire safety is properly managed with emergency procedures in place. Arrangements for first-aid can be audited to ensure provision is adequate, as well as auditing arrangements for the control of contractors. Auditors may cover accident reporting both internally within the organisation and external reporting to the authorities. Auditors should review the arrangements for consultation within the organisation and establish that consultation does take place. Auditors can cover maintenance records of machinery to establish that guarding to machines is maintained, as well as those machines with a statutory requirement for maintenance are maintained. Auditors should also provide recommendations for improving the existing system.*

(c) *The findings from a health and safety audit may be used to distinguish areas of compliance with legislation from those areas that do not meet the necessary standard to comply. The audit should also identify the reasons why non-compliance exists and the nature of the non-compliance. The audit may have distinguished areas of strength from areas of weakness in the management of health and safety. This may facilitate benchmarking by management with other organisations to ensure they are managing health and safety responsibilities in line with industry standards and assist management to direct often scarce resources where they are most required. The findings from the audit can be communicated to staff to ensure that standards are maintained or improved and to indicate that management is motivated to be proactive in the provision of a safe place of work, keeping health and safety on the business agenda. An audit enables management to follow a programme of continual improvement by focusing on eliminating deficiencies.*

Reasons for Poor Marks Achieved by Candidates in Exam

- Confusing an audit with an inspection.
- Giving the reasons for carrying out an audit rather than outlining the key areas an audit should cover.
- Providing insufficient detail to meet the requirements of 'outline' or 'explain'.
- Being unable to explain how the findings from an audit can be used to improve health and safety performance.
- Not being well prepared - you must read and re-read your course notes.

Revision and Examination

The Last Hurdle

Now that you have worked your way through the course material, this section will help you prepare for your NEBOSH examination. This guide contains useful advice on how to approach your revision and the exam itself.

Your NEBOSH Examination

The NEBOSH examination will consist of one question paper which contains one 20-mark question and ten 8-mark questions. You are allowed two hours in which to complete the exam paper and you should answer all the questions.

To pass the exam, you must obtain a minimum of 45% of the total marks available.

If your performance is less than the pass mark then you will be "referred". This means you may resit the examination provided you do so within five years of the original sitting. You may resit as many times as you want within that five-year timescale.

Be Prepared

It may be some time since you last took an exam.

Remember, success in an exam depends mainly on:

- **Revision** – you have to be able to remember, recall and apply the information contained in your course material; and
- **Exam technique** – you have to be able to understand the questions and write good answers in the time available.

Revision and exam technique are skills that can be learnt. We will now look at both of these skills so that you can prepare yourself for the exam. There is a saying that "proper planning and preparation prevents a poor performance". This was never truer than in an exam.

Revision Tips

Using the RRC Course Material

You should read through all of the topics at least once before beginning your revision in earnest. This first read-through should be done slowly and carefully.

Having completed this first revision reading of the course materials, consider briefly reviewing all of it again to check that you understand all of the elements and the important principles that they contain. At this stage, you are not trying to memorise information but simply checking your understanding of the concepts. Make sure that you resolve any outstanding queries with your tutor.

Remember that understanding the information and being able to remember and recall it are two different things. As you read the course material you should **understand** it; in the exam, you have to be able to **remember, recall** and **apply** it. To do this successfully, most people have to go back over the material repeatedly.

Re-read the course material and make notes that summarise important information from each element. **You could use index cards** and create a portable, quick and easy revision aid.

Check your basic knowledge of the content of each element by reading the **Summary**. The Summary should help you recall the ideas contained in the text. If it does not, then you may need to re-visit the appropriate sections of the element.

Using the Syllabus Guide

We recommend that you purchase a copy of the NEBOSH Guide to this course, which contains the syllabus for your exam. If a topic is in the syllabus then it is possible that there will be an examination question on that topic.

Map your level of knowledge and recall against the syllabus guide. Look at the **Content** listed for each element in the syllabus guide. Ask yourself the following question:

If there is a question in the exam about that topic, could I answer it?

You can even score your current level of knowledge for each topic in each element of the syllabus guide and then use your scores as an indication of your personal strengths and weaknesses. For example, if you scored yourself 5 out of 5 for a topic in Element 1, then obviously you don't have much work to do on that subject as you approach the exam. But if you scored yourself 2 out of 5 for a topic in Element 3 then you have identified an area of weakness. Having identified your strengths and weaknesses in this way you can use this information to decide on the topic areas that you need to concentrate on as you revise for the exam.

You could also annotate or highlight sections of the text that you think are important.

Another way of using the syllabus guide is as an active revision aid:

- Pick a topic at random from any of the elements.
- Write down as many facts and ideas that you can recall that are relevant to that particular topic.

Go back to your course material and see what you missed, and fill in the missing areas.

Exam Hints

Success in the exam depends on averaging half marks, or more for each question. Marks are awarded for setting down ideas that are relevant **to the question asked** and demonstrating that you understand what you are talking about. If you have studied your course material thoroughly then this should not be a problem.

One common mistake in answering questions is to go into too much detail on specific topics and fail to deal with the wider issues. If you only cover half the relevant issues, you can only achieve half the available marks. Try to give as wide an answer as you can, without stepping outside the subject matter of the question altogether. Make sure that you cover each issue in appropriate detail in order to demonstrate that you have the relevant knowledge. Giving relevant examples is a good way of doing this.

We mentioned earlier the value of using the syllabus to plan your revision. Another useful way of combining syllabus study with examination practice is to create your own exam questions by adding one of the words you might find at the beginning of an exam question (such as 'explain' or 'identify' or 'outline') in front of the syllabus topic areas. In this way, you can produce a whole range of questions similar to those used in the exam..

Before the Exam

You should:

- Know where the exam is to take place.
- Arrive in good time.
- Bring your examination entry voucher, which
  includes your candidate number, photographic proof of identity, pens, pencils, ruler, etc. (Remember, these must be in a clear plastic bag or wallet.)
- Bring water to drink and sweets to suck, if you want to.

During the Exam

- Read through the whole exam paper before starting work, if that will help settle your nerves. Start with the question of your choice.
- Manage your time. The exam is two hours long. You should attempt to answer all 11 questions in the two hours. To do this, you might spend:
  - 25-30 minutes answering Question 1 (worth 20 marks), and then
  - 8-9 minutes on each of the ten remaining 8-mark questions.

  Check the clock regularly as you write your answers. You should always know exactly where you are, with regard to time.
- As you start each question, read the question carefully. Pay particular attention to the wording of the question to make sure you understand what the examiner is looking for. Note the verbs (command words), such as 'describe', 'explain', 'identify', or 'outline' that are used in the question. These indicate the amount of depth and detail required in your answer. As a general guide:
  - 'Explain' and 'describe' mean give an understanding of/a detailed account of something.
  - 'Outline' means give the key features of something.
  - 'Identify' means give a reference to something (could be name or title).
- Pay close attention to the number of marks available for each question, or part of a question – this usually indicates how many key pieces of information the examiner expects to see in your answer.
- Give examples wherever possible, based either on your own personal experience, or things you have read about. An example can be used to illustrate an idea and demonstrate that you understand what you are saying.
- If you start to run out of time, write your answers in bullet-point or checklist style, rather than failing to answer a question at all.
- Keep your handwriting under control; if the examiner cannot read what you have written, then he or she cannot mark it.
- You will not be penalised for poor grammar or spelling, as long as your answers are clear and can be understood. However, you may lose marks if the examiner cannot make sense of the sentence that you have written.

Suggested Answers

No Peeking!

Once you have worked your way through the study questions in this book, use the suggested answers on the following pages to find out where you went wrong (and what you got right), and as a resource to improve your knowledge and question-answering technique.

Element 1: Foundations in Health and Safety

Question 1

Health and safety has to compete with other management priorities, particularly those associated with the production of goods and services which is the basic rationale of an organisation. It may be seen as an unproductive cost which conflicts with the requirement to keep costs low.

Question 2

(a) Health relates to the physical condition, of both body and mind, of all people at the workplace (employees, contractors and visitors) and their protection from harm in the form of injury or disease.

(b) Safety relates to the conditions at the workplace and applies to the pursuit of a state where the risk of harm has been eliminated or reduced to an acceptable level.

(c) Welfare relates to the general well-being of, primarily, employees at the workplace and the promotion of conditions which help to provide for their needs in respect of health, comfort, and social and personal well-being. This broader concept of welfare is not a specific concern of health and safety at work, but effective health and safety measures may contribute to the conditions which promote it.

Question 3

- Moral (or humanitarian).
- Legal.
- Economic (or financial).

Question 4

- Legal cases indicate how requirements such as "safe place of work" change over the years and act as drivers for an increasing standard of health and safety in the workplace.
- Better staff may only work for employers with high standards of health and safety.
- Widespread access to the media ensures that standards of best practice in the workplace are well known by everyone and therefore establish the norm that people at work expect.

Question 5

- Direct costs: damaged product, repair or replacement of damaged equipment, worker sick pay, production downtime, first aid treatment costs, overtime.
- Indirect costs: low worker morale, damaged business reputation, high staff turnover and associated recruitment costs.

Question 6

(a) Regulations are passed by Parliament and are statutory instruments with full legal status.

(b) ACoPs have special legal status and give guidance on how to comply with the duties set out in **HSWA** and its associated regulations. Failure to comply with an ACoP is not in itself a breach of law, but adhering to the ACoP can be used to prove that compliance has been achieved. Organisations not complying with the ACoP would need to be able to demonstrate that they have achieved or exceeded the legal requirement by other means.

(c) The information contained in HSE guidance notes is purely advisory and has no legal status.

Question 7

(a) The criminal law seeks to punish the wrongdoer (through fines or imprisonment) whilst the civil law seeks restitution for the wrong done, in the form of damages for losses suffered.

(b) Under criminal law, it is for the prosecution to prove the case beyond all reasonable doubt, whereas under civil law it is for the claimant to prove their case on the balance of probabilities.

(c) Criminal actions are brought on behalf of the state. Civil actions are brought by the aggrieved person.

Question 8

Judicial precedent requires that an inferior (lower) court must always follow the decisions of a higher court. Once a judgment has been made in a particular case, that decision will apply in any future cases which match the particular circumstances of the first. Cases which set precedents are invariably determined by the highest courts in the legal system (primarily, the Court of Appeal and the Supreme Court).

Question 9

Regulations (which have the full force of statute law) made under powers given to the Secretary of State (Government Ministers) by Act of Parliament (such as **HSWA**).

Question 10

The common law duties of an employer are established by case law (principally ***Wilsons and Clyde Coal Co. Ltd v. English (1938)***). The employer has a common law duty to provide:

- A safe place of work with safe access to and from it.
- Safe plant and equipment.
- A safe system for doing the work.
- Safe and competent workers.
- Appropriate supervision, information, instruction and training.

Question 11

Prohibition Notices are served in anticipation of danger (risk of serious personal injury) when an inspector is of the opinion that imminent danger exists or will be created in the future.

Improvement Notices are served where a contravention of health and safety law is taking place, or has taken place, and is likely to continue (but is not necessarily dangerous). Prohibition notices do not have timescales allocated, but Improvement notices do – a deadline is set by which the improvement must be made.

Question 12

For an Improvement Notice, an appeal has the effect of suspending the operation of the notice until the appeal is heard or withdrawn. For an appeal against a Prohibition Notice, the prohibition remains in force (unless the person appealing applies for the notice to be suspended and the tribunal gives permission).

Question 13

Employment tribunals hear appeals against enforcement notices (they also hear appeals from safety representatives who feel that their rights have not been upheld by their employer).

Question 14

The three tests are:

- That the defendant was under a duty of care to the claimant (injured party).
- That the duty had been breached.
- That the claimant suffered damage as a direct result of the breach.

Question 15

HSWA is an enabling Act and describes only general duties. The detail of what these duties involve is provided by the various regulations. These regulations are made under the Act.

Question 16

The Health and Safety Executive and the Local Authorities.

Question 17

The powers of inspectors under Section 20 of **HSWA** are as follows:

- To enter premises, at any reasonable time.
- To take along a police officer if they believe they are going to be obstructed.
- To take along technical assistance or equipment if necessary.
- To carry out any necessary examinations and investigations.
- To direct that premises (in whole or in part) or items within the premises are left undisturbed.
- To take photographs, drawings and measurements.
- To take samples of articles or substances and of the atmosphere.
- To dismantle and/or test any item or substance which they think is dangerous.
- To take possession of articles and substances for examination or test, or as evidence in proceedings.
- To take statements from any person who might be able to help in their investigation. Interviewees must answer any questions and sign a statement of their answers, although these are not admissible as evidence in any subsequent proceedings against that person.
- To inspect and copy any document or record considered relevant.
- To receive access to reasonable facilities and assistance in conducting their investigation.
- Any other power necessary to fulfil the duty of their enforcement authority.

Question 18

Absolute duties are those which have to be complied with at all times and in all circumstances – whoever has the responsibility of compliance has no choice about it. The word **shall** is used to impose an absolute duty.

Qualified duties only have to be complied with under certain conditions:

- 'Where practicable' means where it is technically possible, and
- 'Where reasonably practicable' means where the level of risk justifies the cost (measured in time, trouble and money) of reducing the risk.

Question 19

Under Section 2 of the Act, a general duty (2(1)) is placed on the employer "to ensure, so far as is reasonably practicable, the health, safety and welfare at work of all his employees".

The employer's specific duties (2(2)) to his employees are to provide:

- Safe plant and systems of work.
- Safe use, handling, storage and transport of articles and substances.
- Information, instruction, training and supervision.
- A safe workplace and safe access to it and egress from it.
- A safe working environment with adequate welfare facilities.

Question 20

The phrase "so far as is reasonably practicable" means that the degree of risk must be assessed against the sacrifice involved in introducing control measures to eliminate or control the risk. This sacrifice can be measured in terms of financial cost, time and effort. If it can be shown that there is gross disproportion between the risk and the sacrifice then the sacrifice does not have to be made.

Question 21

The employees' duties under **HSWA** (Section 7) are to:

- Take reasonable care for the health and safety of himself and of other persons who may be affected by his acts or omissions at work.
- Co-operate with the employer to enable compliance with legal requirements.

(You could also argue that an employee is covered by the general prohibition in Section 8 not to interfere with things provided for health and safety.)

Question 22

Risk assessments must be recorded where the employer has five or more employees.

Question 23

Procedures to deal with serious and imminent danger.

Question 24

Anyone under the age of 18.

Question 25

- Their health and safety policy.
- Example risk assessments.
- The qualifications of staff.
- Membership of professional organisations.
- Test and maintenance records for plant and equipment.
- References.
- Accident history.
- Enforcement action history.
- Adequate resources.
- Insurance.

Question 26

A notifiable project is one where the construction phase is planned to:

- last over 30 working days and involve more than 20 workers at any one time; or
- involve more than 500 worker days.

Question 27

(a) The client must ensure that:

- Suitably competent designers and contractors are appointed.
- Adequate pre-construction information is provided to the other duty holders.
- Principal designers and principal contractors carry out their duties.
- A Construction Phase Plan for the project is prepared by the principal contractor before work starts.
- The health and safety file is prepared by the principal designer for the building/structure and that this is made available for future reference.
- Suitable welfare facilities are available during the construction phase.
- Notifiable projects are notified to the HSE.

(b) The principal designer must ensure that:

- They plan, manage, monitor and co-ordinate health and safety during the pre-construction phase of the project.
- The client is advised on the bringing together of pre-construction information that will be useful to designers and contractors.
- The design eliminates or minimises health and safety risks created by the project.
- Proper communication, co-operation and co-ordination takes place during the pre-construction phase.
- The Health and Safety File is prepared and passed to the client at the end of the project.

(c) The principal contractor must ensure that:

- The construction phase of the project is adequately planned, managed, monitored and co-ordinated.
- A Construction Phase Plan for the project exists and is kept up to date.
- The site is secure.
- All workers have access to suitable welfare facilities.
- All contractors receive site-specific induction training.
- Workers are consulted on site health and safety issues.

Element 2: Plan

Question 1

Managing for Health and Safety (HSG65) uses the elements of the PDCA cycle Plan-Do-Check-Act.

Question 2

The elements of OHSAS 18001 are:

- Policy (Plan).
- Planning (Plan).
- Implementation and operation (Do).
- Checking and corrective action (Check).
- Management review (Act).
- Continual improvement (Act).

Question 3

When the employer employs less than five people.

Question 4

Section 2(3) of the **Health and Safety at Work, etc. Act 1974**.

Question 5

Because the policy is a reflection of the particular circumstances of each organisation. Thus, any variations in size, nature and organisation of operations, etc. will mean that the health and safety policy will also vary.

Question 6

Statement of intent – a short section outlining the commitment of the organisation to health and safety goals. (What we aim to do.)

Organisation – the organisational responsibilities for health and safety. (Who's going to do it.)

Arrangements – the arrangements in place for managing health and safety and achieving the goals of the organisation as set out in the statement of intent. (How we intend doing it.)

Question 7

The managing director or general manager, a senior director or the chief executive officer, indicating the organisation's commitment at the highest level.

Question 8

To act responsibly and safely at all times, do all they can to prevent injury to themselves and to fellow workers, and co-operate with their employer.

Question 9

The hierarchy of roles and responsibilities for health and safety, and the lines of accountability between them.

Question 10

The circumstances which should give rise to reviews, either of general policy or specific aspects of it, include:

- Changes in the structure of the organisation, and/or changes in key personnel.
- A change in buildings, workplace or worksite.
- When work arrangements change, or new processes are introduced.
- When indicated by a safety audit or a risk assessment.
- Following enforcement action or as the result of the findings from accident investigations.
- Following a change in legislation.
- If consultation with employees or their representatives highlights deficiencies.
- If requested by a third party.

Element 3: Do

Question 1

The four key action areas highlighted in the HSE publication "Leading health and safety at work" (INDG417) are:

- Plan - the board need to set the direction for effective health and safety management.
- Deliver - the policy through an effective management system that ensures that risks are dealt with sensibly, responsibly and proportionately.
- Monitor and report - to the board on the performance of health and safety policy.
- Review of health and safety performance - to allow the board to establish whether the essential health and safety principles are strong.

Question 2

The safety culture of an organisation is the way that everyone within the organisation thinks and feels about health and safety and how this translates into their behaviour. It is either positive or negative.

Question 3

Through the influence of peer group pressure. This is the process by which social groups form in the workplace, group behaviour is established and then social pressure is exerted to force individuals to comply with the group behaviour. There will usually be one or more group leaders who influence the group to a very high degree.

Question 4

The organisation, the job and the individual. The three "human factors" that influence safety-related behaviour.

Question 5

The job factors include:

- Task.
- Workload.
- Environment.
- Display and controls.
- Procedures.

Question 6

Perceptual distortion occurs when something is not recognised for what it is. The brain does not correctly interpret information. This can arise as a result of illness, inexperience, poor education and training, drugs and alcohol, fatigue, etc.

Question 7

Verbal

Limitations	Merits
Language barrier may exist.	Personal.
Jargon may not be understood.	Quick.
Strong accent or dialect may interfere.	Direct.
Background noise may interfere.	Allows for checking of understanding.
Recipient may have poor hearing.	Allows for feedback to be given.
Message may be ambiguous.	Allows for exchange of views.
Recipient may miss information.	Usually allows for additional information to be transmitted by means of tone of voice, facial expression and body language.
Recipient may forget information.	
No written record as proof.	
Poor transmission quality if by telephone or PA system.	

Written

Limitations	Merits
Indirect.	Permanent record.
Takes time to write.	Can be referred back to.
May contain jargon and abbreviations.	Can be written very carefully to avoid use of jargon, abbreviations and ambiguity.
Can be impersonal.	Can be distributed to a wide audience relatively cheaply.
Message may be ambiguous.	
Message may not be read by recipient.	
Language barrier may exist.	
Recipient may not be able to read.	
Immediate feedback is not available.	
Questions cannot be asked.	
Recipient may have impaired vision.	

Question 8

Predominantly in safety signs and hazard-warning labels. Sometimes used on posters.

Question 9

To set out what to do in the event of a fire or other major incident and the general instructions and procedures to be followed for safe movement around the workplace.

Question 10

Whenever there is a significant change to the job which employees are to perform, a significant change to the processes they are to carry out, the introduction of new technology and when the relevant legislation changes.

Question 11

Employees can be involved by:

- Encouraging their participation in safety committees and other safety meetings.
- Asking for their suggestions for improvements (perhaps using a suggestions box or similar scheme).
- Involving them in the selection of PPE and other equipment.
- Providing them with hazard-spotting and defect reporting systems.
- Encouraging their participation in safety tours and inspections, audits, risk assessments, accident investigations and the development of procedures and safe systems of work.
- Assisting in the presentation of safety training, and the supervision/mentoring of new employees, particularly young persons.
- Designing or involvement in the selection of safety posters.

Question 12

Directly, or through elected representatives (Representatives of Employee Safety) in a non-unionised workplace. Through Trade Union Safety Representatives in a unionised workplace.

Question 13

Safety representatives have the right to:

- Carry out an inspection of the workplace (at least once every three months).
- Examine the causes of accidents.
- Examine and copy records and documents relating to health and safety.
- Receive information from HSE inspectors.
- Investigate complaints about health and safety.
- Make representations to the employer.
- Be consulted on health and safety matters.
- Time off with pay to perform their functions.
- Time off with pay for appropriate training.
- Reasonable facilities to perform their functions.

Question 14

Employers have to establish a safety committee when requested to do so in writing by two or more TU safety representatives. The employer then has three months to set the committee up.

Question 15

Hazards will always exist in the workplace and usually it is not possible to eliminate them. Risk can be controlled and reduced. This is the central point of health and safety management.

Question 16

The aim of risk assessment is to eliminate hazards or reduce risk to an acceptable level. The objectives are to prevent personal injury and ill health; to achieve legal compliance and to reduce the costs associated with losses.

Question 17

Inspection, job/task analysis, analysis of incident data, examination of legislative requirements and associated guidance, examination of manufacturers' information.

Question 18

Physical, chemical, biological, ergonomic and psychological.

Question 19

Identify the hazards, decide who might be harmed and how, evaluate the risks and decide on precautions, record the findings and implement them, and review the assessment and update if necessary.

Question 20

Maintenance staff, cleaners, young workers, lone workers, new and expectant mothers and disabled staff.

Question 21

The likelihood of harm occurring and the severity of that harm.

Question 22

Residual risk is the level of risk remaining after the application of safety precautions.

Question 23

- Elimination of the hazard.
- Substitution.
- Engineering controls.
- Administrative controls.
- Personal protective equipment.

Question 24

Factors which might trigger the review of a risk assessment include changes in legislation, a significant change in work practices and processes, installation of new machinery and equipment, new information becoming available on the hazards/risks, recurring accidents or patterns of ill health, enforcement action, results of monitoring/auditing, or employment of a category of personnel (e.g. disabled) not previously taken into account.

Question 25

(a) Mandatory action – must put litter in bins.
(b) Prohibition – not drinking water.
(c) Safe condition – drinking water.
(d) Warning – radiation hazard.

Question 26

When it has not been possible to eliminate the hazard or reduce risk to acceptable levels by the use of engineering controls, working methods or administrative controls. PPE is a last resort.

Question 27

The missing principles are:

- Control the hazards at source, rather than taking measures to control the risk in the wider workplace.
- Giving priority to collective protective measures over individual protective measures.
- Giving appropriate instructions to employees.

Question 28

Internal data sources include: accident records; medical records; risk assessments; maintenance reports; joint inspections with safety representatives; audits, surveys, sampling and tours; safety committee meeting minutes.

External data sources include: national legislation (e.g. regulations), safety data sheets from manufacturers and suppliers, enforcing authority publications such as Codes of Practice and Guidance Notes, manufacturers'/suppliers' maintenance manuals, National/International standards (BS, BS-EN and ISO standards), information from local safety groups, information from trade associations, information from journals and magazines.

Question 29

A safe system of work is a formal procedure which results from a systematic examination of the tasks of a work process in order to identify all the hazards and define methods of working which eliminate those hazards or minimise the risks associated with them.

Question 30

Involvement enables employees to gain a deeper understanding of hazards and risks, and of the way in which safe systems of work will minimise those risks. It also encourages ownership of key controls by the employees involved in their development.

Question 31

Technical or engineering controls are those which are applied directly to the hazard itself in order to minimise the risk. Procedural controls define the way in which work should be carried out in relation to the hazard. Behavioural controls define how the individual operator or groups of workers must act in relation to the hazard.

Question 32

Because only people who have been given appropriate training and instruction should be allowed to undertake the work. Supervision is necessary to ensure that staff follow their instructions and training.

Question 33

Permits to work are formal documents specifying the work to be done, hazards, and the precautions to be taken. Work can only start when safe procedures have been defined and put into place. The permit provides a clear written record, signed by a responsible manager or supervisor, that all foreseeable hazards have been considered and all the necessary actions have been taken. It should usually be in the possession of the person in charge of the operation before work can begin.

Question 34

Issue, receipt, clearance/return to service, cancellation.

Question 35

The main objective of an emergency procedure is to ensure the safety and health of staff and others who might be affected by the emergency. In some instances, minimising other losses associated with the emergency will also be a priority. Preventing an escalation of the emergency may also be important.

Question 36

Fire, bomb threat, spillage of a hazardous chemical, release of a toxic gas, outbreak of disease, severe weather or flooding, multiple casualty accident.

Question 37

- The size of organisation.
- Number of employees.
- Distribution of the workforce (e.g. number of buildings on a site, number of floors, etc.).
- The type of business and what hazards are inherent in it (an office is different from a foundry).
- Remoteness of the site from emergency medical services.
- Provision for non-employees, e.g. shoppers, schoolchildren.
- Needs of specific groups of employees (e.g. trainees, young workers, disabled persons).
- Cover for first aiders during annual leave.
- Shift patterns.
- Peripatetic employees.

Element 4: Check

Question 1

Reactive monitoring is where accidents and other incidents are investigated to find out what went wrong and identify action to prevent recurrence. It also involves the use of accident statistics to identify trends and patterns in accident history. Active monitoring is where existing conditions are inspected to identify and correct sub-standard matters before any sort of incident occurs.

Question 2

Systematic monitoring involves the planned, regular examination of standards in the workplace as a matter of routine.

Question 3

The information for reactive monitoring might come from accident and incident reports, accident and incident investigations, issues raised by employees and failings identified by external agencies (e.g. insurance companies or enforcement authorities).

Question 4

The purpose of workplace inspections is to ensure that the control measures are operating effectively and that they are appropriate to current conditions in the workplace.

Question 5

Safety inspections are routine examinations of workplace conditions carried out by a competent person(s) (e.g. the weekly inspection of a workshop by the workshop supervisor). Safety tours are high-profile inspections carried out by a team of people, including managers.

Question 6

Senior management has responsibility for ensuring that effective workplace inspection regimes are in place and are operated effectively. This will include receiving reports and overseeing/agreeing action. In addition, the visible involvement of senior managers in inspections is to be encouraged for the commitment it demonstrates towards safety and the effect on the promotion of a positive health and safety culture.

Question 7

Checklists help to ensure a consistent, systematic and comprehensive approach to checking all the safety elements to be covered during an inspection.

Question 8

The introductory part of an inspection report should set the scene, outlining what the report is about, why it has been written (the aim), when and where the inspection took place and who carried it out.

Question 9

The prime purpose of an accident investigation is to find the cause, with the intention of preventing a recurrence.

Question 10

- Gather factual information about the event.
- Analyse that information and draw conclusions about the immediate and root causes.
- Identify suitable control measures.
- Plan the remedial actions.

Question 11

The categories of staff might include the immediate line manager (of the injured person or of the area where the event took place), a member of management, a safety representative, a safety officer, an engineer or technical expert if relevant.

Question 12

The types of record to be consulted might be:

- Inspection and maintenance records.
- Risk assessments.
- Safe system of work or permit to work.
- Environmental measurements.
- Medical records.
- General and specific safety reports and analysis which relate to the circumstances.
- Training and other personnel records.
- Minutes of safety committee meetings.

Question 13

Unsafe acts and unsafe conditions.

Question 14

Immediate Causes	Root Causes
Mechanical failure (faulty brakes)	Inadequate maintenance procedures
Driver failed to see pedestrian	Lighting or weather conditions
Pedestrian not wearing high-visibility jacket	No rule about high-visibility jackets, or not enforced
Driver's vision restricted by goods	Lack of housekeeping arrangements Lack of banksman
Human error on part of driver or pedestrian	Lack of training and awareness

Question 15

The involved employee or colleagues if they are not able to. In some circumstances it might be the first aider who gave treatment. It might be the immediate line manager. Company policy will dictate.

Question 16

To identify underlying causes of accidents and to provide information about trends and other patterns in workplace accidents.

Question 17

Depending on circumstances, the result of an individual accident investigation would be communicated to the victim, their immediate manager and the local safety representative. It may also be necessary to inform other managers in the organisation, including senior management and the safety committee. For reportable incidents, the results might also be notified to the enforcement agency.

Question 18

Fatalities, specified injuries, over-seven-day injuries, dangerous occurrences, and reportable occupational diseases.

Question 19

Fatalities and specified injuries must be reported to the HSE Incident Contact Centre as soon as possible after the event by telephone or online form.

All other injuries, diseases and dangerous occurrences must be reported as soon as possible using the online F2508 form.

The exception is over-seven-day injuries that need to be reported by online form within 15 days of the incident.

Question 20

For at least three years.

Question 21

Carpal tunnel syndrome; severe cramp of the hand or forearm, occupational dermatitis, hand-arm vibration syndrome, occupational asthma, tendonitis or tenosinovitis of the hand or forearm, an occupational cancer, and any disease attributed to an occupational exposure to a biological agent.

Question 22

The types of information may include:

- Accident documentation about other, similar, incidents.
- Risk assessments relating to drilling work in that particular workplace.
- Inspection and maintenance records in respect of the particular equipment and guard, and others in the area.
- Other recent and relevant documentation relating to the use of guards, reporting of faults, employee history (including training records), etc.

Question 23

The following action should be taken:

- Make area safe (in some circumstances this might need to be done first so there is no risk to those giving assistance).
- Ensure first aid and then medical treatment for the victim.
- Isolate the scene so evidence is not disturbed.
- Inform next of kin.
- Notify enforcing authority.
- Inform safety representatives, and issue internal information.
- Arrange any necessary counselling or support.
- Advise insurers.
- Set up investigation team:
  - Collect evidence, including photographs, measurements, etc.
  - Take statements from witnesses.
  - Determine immediate and root causes.
  - Report, making recommendations to prevent recurrence.
- Implement recommendations, revise work procedures and risk assessments.
- Monitor situation and review as necessary.

Element 5: Act

Question 1

Health and safety auditing is the structured process of collecting independent information on the efficiency, effectiveness and reliability of the total health and safety management system and drawing up plans for corrective action.

Question 2

Differences between Audits and Workplace Inspections	
Audit	Workplace Inspection
Has the aim of assessing the health and safety management system of an organisation.	Has the aim of assessing the use and effectiveness of control measures.
A long process involving the examination of the entire management system.	A relatively short process looking at practices in part of the workplace.
Based primarily on review of documentary evidence, backed up by some observations and interviews of personnel at all levels.	Primarily based on observations, perhaps involving limited scrutiny of paperwork and interview of operators.
Long, comprehensive report that records areas of concern and weaknesses in the management system.	Short report identifying key corrective actions required.
Detailed planning required; requires considerable resources.	Only limited planning; and main resource required is the inspectors' time.
Typically done annually.	Usually done on a weekly, monthly, or quarterly frequency.
Aims to improve systems at a high level, with ultimate effect of cascading down to operating level. Is a strategic tool, addressing long-term progress.	Focuses on activities and equipment at operational level, though remedial actions may address system faults.

Question 3

To ensure that the organisational arrangements, health and safety standards and operational systems and measures are working effectively and, where they are not, to identify the corrective actions needed.

Question 4

Senior management should review the operation of the health and safety management system to ensure that it is being fully implemented and that it remains suitable for achieving the organisation's policy and objectives.

Reviews should be instigated by senior managers but also involve managers, supervisors, and occupational health and safety specialists. It may also be appropriate to involve safety representatives or representatives of workplace safety in the review process, particularly if the health and safety committee is the forum where the review takes place.

Question 5

Perhaps:

- Monthly reviews of individuals, supervisors or sections.
- Three-monthly reviews of departments.
- Annual reviews of sites or the organisation as a whole.

Question 6

- Minutes of the review.
- Documented revisions to the health and safety policy and health and safety objectives.
- Specific corrective actions for individual managers with target dates for completion.
- Specific improvement actions with assigned responsibilities and target dates for completion.
- Date for review of corrective action.
- Areas of emphasis to be reflected in the planning of future management system audits.